PRAEGER LIBRARY OF U.S. GOVERNMENT DEPARTMENTS
AND AGENCIES

The Agricultural Research Service

PRAEGER LIBRARY OF U.S. GOVERNMENT DEPARTMENTS
AND AGENCIES

Consulting Editors

ERNEST S. GRIFFITH

Former University Professor and Dean Emeritus, School of International Service, American University; former Director, Legislative Reference Service, Library of Congress; and author of *The American System of Government* and *The Modern Government in Action*

HUGH LANGDON ELSBREE

Former Chairman, Department of Political Science, Dartmouth College; former Managing Editor, *American Political Science Review;* former Director, Legislative Reference Service, Library of Congress

The Agricultural Research Service

Ernest G. Moore

FREDERICK A. PRAEGER, *Publishers*
New York · Washington · London

FREDERICK A. PRAEGER, PUBLISHERS
111 Fourth Avenue, New York, N.Y. 10003, U.S.A.
77-79 Charlotte Street, London W.1, England

Published in the United States of America in 1967
by Frederick A. Praeger, Inc., Publishers

© 1967 by Ernest G. Moore

Library of Congress Catalog Card Number: 67-22294

Printed in the United States of America

Acknowledgments

So many friends in the Agricultural Research Service and in other agencies of the U.S. Department of Agriculture graciously supplied helpful information for this book that I find it difficult to name one without naming all. However, I am especially indebted to Dr. Byron T. Shaw, former administrator of the Agricultural Research Service, for many helpful suggestions. His counsel and judgment were invaluable throughout the work.

Mrs. Stella English, a long-time associate in the Agricultural Research Service, read the entire manuscript and made countless editorial suggestions. For her patience and enthusiasm, my sincere thanks.

ERNEST G. MOORE

Preface

When I began work on this book, I discovered that many people felt that it should contain a defense—or at least an explanation—of the part agricultural research had played in building up those huge surpluses of farm products that we used to hear so much about. My first reaction was to dismiss this argument because (1) it was fallacious, and (2) the surpluses no longer existed.

More thought on the question, however, and more discussion with friends outside of government finally led me to the conclusion that it might be well to bring up this matter in the beginning, so that it would not be lurking in the background throughout the book. The question in the minds of many people a few years ago was this: Why should the federal government spend money for research that makes possible greater production of farm products at the same time it is spending large sums for programs to hold down production? A few even went so far as to recommend that the government should declare a moratorium on all agricultural research except that aimed at improved marketing and at discovering new uses for farm products.

There is no simple answer to such an argument, which is based upon a lack of understanding of the nature of research. Scientific knowledge is cumulative; each discovery is based upon a previous discovery and provides the foundation for still another. Research cannot be turned off and on like a light switch. Without continuity in research on pest control, for example, the benefits of many years' efforts would quickly disappear, and insects would harvest our crops.

No one can deny that agricultural research pointed the way to better soil management, better use of fertilizers, better strains of seed, better control of insects, diseases, and weeds, and better methods of harvesting, storage, and transportation of farm products to markets. And all of these added up to greater production. Government price supports, begun in 1933, certainly played a part, many would say a large part, in the build-up of surpluses, and the low prices received by farmers undoubtedly caused many of them to farm more intensively in an effort to keep income ahead of expenses.

Although it is impossible to say to what degree research was responsible for the surpluses, it is certain that without research there would have been no surpluses. Neither would we have had the abundance, to which we have become so accustomed that we now take it for granted.

Fortunately, we now also take research for granted. Since the dawn of the space age, it is no longer popular to suggest that we can get along with less emphasis on science. The trend is in the other direction, and this applies to research in agriculture as well as to research in space and atomic energy. In recent years, Congress has been liberal in appropriating funds for agricultural research.

By the spring of 1967, most of the surpluses had disappeared —through adjustments in production, increased exports for dollars, and aid to needy nations. With so many hungry people in the world and a national policy to help those people to help themselves, it is unlikely that surplus food production will ever again cause responsible people to suggest a moratorium on agricultural reseach.

The Agricultural Research Service and its parent organizations in the U.S. Department of Agriculture have played a major role in making us one of the best-fed nations in history. These agencies have also made great contributions to human health and comfort, through research on livestock diseases and on such insects as houseflies and mosquitoes. Yet the majority of people living in urban areas know little or nothing about the Agricultural Research Service. It is unfortunate that an agency that touches the lives of so many people every day and generates so much needed information should be so little known by those it seeks to serve.

The purpose of this book, therefore, is to introduce the Agricultural Research Service to many who might not otherwise learn about this agency and the interesting and significant work it does.

Contents

CONTENTS

CHART

THE STRUCTURE OF THE AGRICULTURAL RESEARCH

A section of photographs follows page 84.

The Agricultural Research Service

I

Agricultural Research—Yesterday and Today

The roots of the Agricultural Research Service go deep into American history. Even in the earliest colonial period, settlers were making simple experiments designed to help provide a year-round supply of food. The colonists had to contend with soils and climate different from those they had known. In fact, they had to learn a new kind of agriculture. In Europe, they had planted grain by broadcasting the seed. In North America, they learned from the Indians to plant corn, beans, and potatoes in hills, pulling the soil up around the plants as they grew.

George Washington was a farmer as well as a soldier and a statesman. Of the several farms he owned, Mount Vernon became the most famous. This historic estate was probably the nation's first experimental farm. In his diary for April 14, 1760, Washington recorded the plan for a test of various soil treatments to discover their effect on yields of wheat and other grains he was growing at the time. In the experiment, he used marl from one of his fields, mud from a creek bottom, soil from a gully, and manure from horses, cows, and sheep. Each was mixed with soil from the same field and placed in boxes. Washington personally sowed seed in each of the boxes. The diary then relates that "two or three hours after sowing . . . and about an hour before sunset I watered all of them equally alike with water that had been standing in a tub abt two hours exposed to the sun."

Washington the farmer developed a superior strain of wheat by selecting seeds of the best plants for the next year's planting. He improved his sheep by carefully selecting the best animals for breeding. He was the nation's first mule breeder. He also diversified his crops, practiced soil conservation, and tried new machinery. It is not surprising that the first formal proposal for an agricultural agency in the new federal government came from this man. In his last annual message to Congress, in 1796, he proposed that a Board of Agriculture be established to collect results of experiments and observations and to pass this information on to appropriate officials in the states. Although agricultural leaders supported the idea, there was not enough interest in Congress to transform the proposal into law.

However, a large number of agricultural societies had already been organized to encourage improved farming methods, and a few agricultural journals had begun publication. The societies and the journals continued to emphasize the need for an agency such as Washington had suggested. Agricultural experiments were being conducted in England and in Germany, and U.S. agricultural leaders urged that results of these experiments be made available to our farmers in language they could understand. Taking note of this interest, President John Quincy Adams proposed legislation to create an agricultural agency—but again Congress took no action.

Other famous early Americans tried to promote agricultural research. Like Washington, Thomas Jefferson was a farmer who liked to experiment; his Monticello was another of the nation's pioneering experimental farms. While traveling in Italy in 1787, Jefferson sent home seed of upland rice—although in so doing he was violating Italian law, which sought to protect growers against foreign competition. Benjamin Franklin, while in France as agent for the colony of Pennsylvania, also saw the possibility of helping colonial farmers by introducing new or improved crops. He was later instrumental in persuading the State Department to instruct all consuls abroad to send back seeds of crops they thought might be useful here.

Although substantial amounts of seed came from the consuls, there was a large increase in such imports following the appointment of Henry L. Ellsworth as commissioner of patents in 1836. Ellsworth had traveled extensively in the prairie states and was impressed with their tremendous agricultural possibilities. In his new post he encouraged, and personally paid for, the distribution to U.S. farmers of seeds and plants from abroad.

A decade of industrial development paralleled Ellsworth's dedication to agriculture. The years 1830–40 saw the invention of the threshing machine, the mowing machine, the reaper, and the steel plow. Railroads stretching from the East Coast to the Mississippi River provided transportation for farm products to centers of population. These and other developments pointed to the growing importance of food production and the need for help from the federal government.

Congress finally took action in 1839, appropriating $1,000 to the Commissioner of Patents for "the collection of agricultural statistics and other agricultural purposes." At that time, appropriated funds were available until spent, and this first appropriation lasted for three years. Another $1,000 was appropriated in 1842, $2,000 in 1843 and 1844, and $5,000 in 1845.

Experimentation was first suggested in the 1856 appropriations bill, which provided for "collection of agricultural statistics, investigations for promoting agriculture and rural economy, and the procurement and distribution of cuttings and seeds."

Between 1839, when the first appropriation was made, and 1862, when the Department of Agriculture was established, no more than a beginning had been made in scientific work for agriculture. The principal activities of the Agricultural Division of the Patent Office, established by Ellsworth, had been to distribute seeds and publications compiled from various sources. More important had been its success in calling attention to the need for more knowledge about farming in the United States.

The Beginnings of Research

The U.S. Department of Agriculture came into existence in 1862, in the midst of the Civil War, when President Abraham Lincoln signed his name to an act establishing "at the seat of the Government of the United States a Department of Agriculture, the general design and duties of which shall be to acquire and diffuse among the people of the United States useful information on subjects connected with agriculture in the most general and comprehensive sense of that word, and to procure, propagate, and distribute among the people new and valuable seeds and plants."

In effect, the Agricultural Division of the Patent Office became the new Department of Agriculture. Isaac Newton, head of the Division, was chosen by Lincoln as the first commissioner of agriculture. Newton's formal education had ended with the common schools of Delaware County, Pennsylvania, but he had become a successful farmer and large-scale landowner.

One of Newton's first appointees was William Saunders, a native of Scotland and an able landscape gardener, who was named superintendent of the propagating garden. A tract of land in the District of Columbia just south of the Baltimore and Ohio canal was assigned to the Department for propagating and experimental work, but the tract was used as a cattle yard by the Army until the Civil War ended in 1865. It consisted of the area in the southwest quadrant of Washington now bounded by Twelfth and Fourteenth streets and Constitution and Independence avenues. The main building of the Department was located at the south end of this tract, which is now a part of the famous mall that extends from the Washington Monument to the Capitol.

Another early appointment was that of Charles M. Weatherill as chemist. Many scientists and laymen believed that the road to better farming lay in chemical analysis of crops, soils, manures, and other products, such as lime or marl, added to the soil. Among the first crops analyzed were grapes—as the potential basis of a wine industry—and sugars from various crops. The scarcity of sugar during the Civil War had created great interest in the possibility of producing sugar from crops that could be grown on the new lands of the West.

Although Dr. Weatherill was the first scientist appointed after the Department was established, he was preceded by a well-known entomologist, Townend Glover, who had been appointed in 1854 by Commissioner of Patents Charles Mason to take charge of collecting information on seeds, fruits, and insects.

A Division of Botany was created in 1868 to classify and preserve the herbarium material that had been collected in various government expeditions, and a year later Charles C. Parry became the Department's first botanist. Its first veterinarian, Professor John Gamgee, was appointed in 1868 to direct research on tick fever, a disease that caused heavy losses of cattle in northern states that had been in contact with those from the South. (Cattle from Texas and neighboring states were driven to northern markets and often came in contact with local cattle along the way.) Congress provided $15,000 for this first attack on tick fever. Chapter IV tells how tick fever was later conquered by research, leading to one of the greatest discoveries ever made by agricultural scientists.

Plant diseases were recognized as a major field of study in 1871, when Thomas Taylor was appointed head of a new Division of Microscopy. This designation for a division now seems rather quaint, but there were relatively few people in 1871 who were proficient with a microscope. Taylor had charge of all work with microscopes in the Department, and he is credited with making several discoveries in plant pathology. However, the use of microscopes had grown to such an extent by 1895 that the division was abolished, and investigators used microscopes as they did other laboratory equipment.

Important advances were made in the scientific work of the Department during the administration of William Gates Le Duc, who became commissioner of agriculture in 1877. Charles V. Riley served as entomologist from 1878 to 1894, except for two years, when he headed the U.S. Entomological Commission. While working for the commission, he made an exhaustive study of grasshoppers, which constantly threatened to devour crops of the settlers in the West. In this and other studies, he laid the foundation for much of the Department's later, excellent work on insect control.

Le Duc's wish to make the United States as nearly self-sufficient as possible led to special efforts to produce sugar and tea. Peter Collier, who served as chemist from 1878 to 1883, directed studies to improve yields of sugar from cane and to make the production of sugar from beets, corn, and sorghum commercially feasible. The work with corn and sorghum was not successful, but that with beets helped to lay groundwork for a sugar beet industry in the West. Congress provided funds for an experimental tea farm at Summerville, South Carolina, where work continued for many years before it was finally abandoned.

Control of livestock diseases was emphasized when England and other countries in Europe began to embargo live cattle from the United States because of the danger of spreading diseases to their herds. Le Duc urged Congress to establish a Division of Veterinary Science in the Department to bring these diseases under control. Congress appropriated $10,000 for this work in 1878 and a like amount in 1880.

By 1884, the animal disease problem had become so acute that Congress recognized the need for more research as well as for strict enforcement of an Act passed in 1873 to regulate the transportation of animals. The Bureau of Animal Industry was accordingly created by Act of Congress, and Dr. Daniel E. Salmon became its first chief. This gave the Department its first scientific bureau.

Additional progress in scientific work was made under the leadership of Norman J. Colman, the last commissioner and the first Secretary of Agriculture. Two organizational units that were to become important in the Department's research on plants came into existence in 1886: the Division of Pomology, which collected various fruit varieties and published reports on potentially valuable varieties and the Section of Vegetable Pathology, which began studies of grape and peach diseases.

Although scientific efforts in the early years of the Department were useful, very little bona fide research was done before 1890. Most of the scientists were kept busy on service work, analyzing soils, marl, manures, and crops, classifying plants, making observations on crops and insects, trying new crops, and answering inquiries from farmers. This work was necessary, but it was not research.

The scientists were unusually able men. Many had been trained at some of the best universities in the country, several held advanced degrees, and a few had studied in leading universities of Europe. Most of these men wrote profusely about their work, and much of their writing appeared in annual reports.

Looking back from the vantage point of the 1960's, it seems a shame that so much time and effort were spent on research assignments that were doomed to failure. A good example was the long effort to produce silk in this country. The first experiments made it clear that silkworms could be grown here, and the native mulberry trees offered a good food supply for the worms. The difficulty lay in finding machine methods that would substitute for cheap Oriental labor in removing the silk threads from the cocoons and for other steps in processing the raw silk. It was only after many years of failure that Congress and the Department finally gave up on silk.

Also futile was the effort to produce sugar from corn. A French scientist had reported that if ears of corn were removed before ripening, the sugar content of the stalks would be greatly increased. This report stimulated studies that lasted for many years but met with no success.

A good share of the enthusiasm—and all the money—that made these fruitless efforts possible came from members of Congress, who understandably wanted their young nation to become self-sufficient in such basic requirements as food and fiber. The need for self-sufficiency, especially apparent in wartime, had stimulated efforts to grow cotton in the northern states during the Civil War, as it was to stimulate attempts during World War II to produce rubber experimentally from dandelions, the desert shrub guayule, and other plants.

It would be a mistake, however, to assume that no practical gains resulted from these seemingly futile efforts. The sugar experiments failed with corn but helped to increase yields from sugar cane in the South and to establish a sugar beet industry in the western states. The work on sweet sorghum went on for many years without much success, but by 1966 new varieties had been developed that promised to produce as much sugar per acre as sugar cane. Different harvest times for these two crops make it possible to utilize the same processing plants for both and thus cut overhead costs materially.

But immediate, measurable results are not the final answer in science. History abounds with illustrations of the fact that all knowledge is potentially useful to man. A story is told about the great English scientist Michael Faraday. At one of his lectures on electromagnetic induction, a lady in the audience asked what was the use of the information. Faraday replied with a question of his own: "Madam, what is the use of a newborn baby?"

Federal Grants to State Agricultural Experiment Stations

Great impetus was given to agricultural research in the last quarter of the nineteenth century by passage of the Hatch Act in 1887, which provided annual grants of money to establish and support state experiment stations in the land-grant colleges. The Homestead Act of 1862 had authorized large grants of public lands to the states as endowments for colleges to teach agriculture and mechanic arts, and by 1887 most of the states had established such colleges.

The courses in agriculture were based on courses in the natural sciences as taught in the leading universities of Europe. Too often experimental results cited in such courses came from European experiment stations and had little application to the United States. Educators agreed that the courses had little to offer students who wished to become farmers. The obvious solution to this problem was the establishment of experiment stations at U.S. land-grant colleges. Several states had already established stations, but none had sufficient funds to operate successfully.

The first state to establish its own experiment station was Connecticut, whose legislature in 1875 provided $700 per quarter for two years with the understanding that the funds would be used to employ scientific men to carry on experiments. A fund of $1,000 had been raised from private sources in the expectation that it would be supplemented by state funds.

California was the next state to provide for an experiment station. When Eugene W. Hilgard joined the university staff as professor of agriculture in 1875, the regents gave him $250 for each of two years for "an industrial survey and experiment station." North Carolina followed in 1877, Massachusetts in 1878, and both New Jersey and New York (at Cornell) in 1880. Altogether, fourteen states were operating experiment stations on meager funds when the Hatch Act was passed in 1887.

The Hatch Act was historic in that it established a policy of federal aid to the states for research. The initial amounts of money were small, only $15,000 to each state, but the long-range implications of the policy are difficult to exaggerate. The Act had an immediate effect. The funds came at a crucial time; without them, some of the stations might not have weathered the financial drought and others might not have been established for many years to come. The most important effect on agricultural research was the formal link established between the Department of Agriculture and the states. Over the last eighty years this partnership has produced results that powered one of the greatest advances in agriculture ever made by any nation.

From the moment that President Lincoln signed the Land Grant College Act of 1862, it was inevitable that the agricultural colleges would have their own experiment stations. Few of the states were able or willing to support stations on a scale sufficient to be of much help to farmers. Agricultural leaders, therefore, began a campaign to have the federal government subsidize state stations. In the meantime, a few states established experiment stations of their own, some of which were operated partly or wholly with donated funds. Organized efforts were made to get Congress to act, and by 1882 subsidy bills were being introduced. Secretary of Agriculture Colman and many state leaders kept the idea constantly before Congress until 1887, when the Hatch Act was passed and signed into law.

The Department Raised to Cabinet Level

Another important piece of legislation was the act passed by Congress in 1889 that gave Cabinet rank to the Department of Agriculture. As with most of the other laws concerning agriculture, the passage of this act was preceded by several years of public discussion. The two large national farmers' organizations, the National Grange and the Farmers Alliance, as well as the farm publications, strongly supported the added recognition to agriculture. The first bill to elevate the Department to Cabinet rank was introduced in the House in 1874. After five years of public discussion and congressional debate, the measure was passed and signed by President Grover Cleveland.

During congressional debate on the measure, there was much criticism of the Department, especially in the Senate. Senator William E. Chandler of New Hampshire declared that cabinet posts should be reserved for essential activities of the government and that fostering agriculture was in no sense essential to the government of the country. In a debate on earlier legislation, which eventually passed the House in 1882 and 1884, the chairman of the House Committee on Agriculture had said:

> The controlling idea in the creation of the Department is that our wide domain should be tested, to ascertain what can be most successfully produced in its various sections. Experiments in this direction cannot be profitably conducted forever. Sooner or later the work of the Department should be closed, and meanwhile I cannot see why the farmer should not . . . learn to experiment for himself . . . and act for himself without reference to government aid.

Cabinet rank made no change in the Department except to give it added prestige. The commissioner of Agriculture became the Secretary of Agriculture, and a position of assistant secretary was authorized. Within a short time, a new administration took office and the President named Jeremiah Rusk as Secretary and Edwin Willits, president of Michigan Agricultural College, as assistant secretary. This was the first time a high official of the Department had been named from one of the land-grant (agricultural) colleges. It was a wise move, helping to cement relations between the colleges and the Department in their early years. Rusk made Willits responsible for all scientific work in the Department, which assured top-level support to research.

Rusk believed it necessary to make results of Department research available to all farmers and others who were interested. As a first step, the Office of Experiment Stations, created in 1888 to administer the Hatch Act funds, issued two publications in a series designated as Farmers Bulletins. A few years later, Congress authorized a yearly publication on the work of the Department that became known as *The Yearbook of Agriculture.*

A milestone in the regulatory work of the Department was

the initiation of meat inspection by the federal government during this period. Despite the eradication of pleuropneumonia in livestock, European countries still discriminated against American meat. The Meat Inspection Act of August 30, 1890, supplemented by a second act the following year, required the inspection of cattle intended for export, live cattle whose meat was to be exported, and cattle, sheep, and hogs whose meat was to be sold in interstate commerce. An Inspection Division was established in the Bureau of Animal Industry on April 1, 1891, to carry out this work. A Quarantine Division was created in the bureau at the same time to enforce livestock quarantine regulations.

The third Secretary of Agriculture, Julius Sterling Morton, served from March, 1893, to March, 1897, a period of serious national depression. In his zeal to cut expenses, Morton reduced the number of Department clerks and cut the salaries of those he retained. With the exception of five women, all of whom must have been key employees, no woman employee of the Department of Agriculture could earn more than $1,200 a year. Morton refused to distribute seeds, feeling that it was a waste of money. He was severely reprimanded by Congress, who ordered him to resume seed distribution, but he continued to be quite critical of this activity.

Morton will be remembered for his interest in supporting human nutrition research at a time when he was practicing severe economies in other areas. At his suggestion, Congress appropriated $10,000 in 1895 for this work, which was placed under the direction of Wilbur O. Atwater, first chief of the Office of Experiment Stations.

In spite of these strict economies, two new divisions were created in the Department on July 1, 1895—a Dairy Division in the Bureau of Animal Industry and a Division of Agrostology to study grasses and forage plants.

In the closing years of the nineteenth century, farmers were in financial trouble and their leaders were looking to Washington for help. For all practical purposes, the frontier was gone. Farmers were no longer able to move westward and stake out new claims. Land still available required a considerable outlay of capital, and money was hard to get. There was much feeling that the best way out of these difficulties was through research that would help farmers to get greater yields and to cut costs of production.

Agricultural research in the United States was helped tremendously by events elsewhere. In 1900 Gregor Mendel's monumental work explaining the laws of inheritance was rediscovered after a period of forty years. In 1902 the Dutch botanist Hugo De Vries announced his theory of mutations in the evolution of plants. In this country, Thomas Hunt Morgan applied the term "genes" to the parts of chromosomes that determine certain hereditary characteristics. The influence of these men on plant research in the Department and in the state experiment stations was very great.

Even before this knowledge became available, our agricultural scientists were demonstrating that research could provide some of the answers that farmers needed. Willet M. Hays of Minnesota, for example, had already developed several new varieties of disease-resistant wheat and released them to farmers in his state. The stage was being set for science to play a larger role in farming. All that was needed was a forceful leader able to obtain support for research from the White House and from Congress. He appeared in 1897 as the new Secretary of Agriculture, "Tama Jim" Wilson of Tama, Iowa.

Expansion of Research and Regulatory Work

Secretary James Wilson (called Tama Jim to distinguish him from his fellow Iowan "Jefferson Jim" Wilson) was ideally suited for his job by temperament, training, and experience. Born in Scotland, he came with his family to the United States at an early age and grew up on an Iowa farm. He attended Iowa

Agricultural College for a time but was largely self-educated through wide reading. He owned and operated a farm and served three terms in the state legislature before being elected to Congress. After three terms in the House, he retired and began to write extensively on agriculture. One of the regents of Iowa Agricultural College, he served three years as professor of agriculture and director of the experiment station. In 1897 he left the college to become Secretary of Agriculture under President William McKinley.

Wilson believed in research, and his experience as a congressman had taught him how to get along with members of Congress. Because of his talent for explaining the business of his Department to congressional committees, agricultural appropriations increased from about $3 million in 1898 to almost $25 million in 1913, Wilson's last year as Secretary. His sixteen years in the Cabinet—under Presidents William McKinley, Theodore Roosevelt, and William Howard Taft—established a record for unbroken service that has never been equaled. His interest in scientific work made him a frequent visitor in the Department laboratories. He knew all the scientists and what they were doing. Under previous secretaries, the assistant secretary had supervised research and regulatory work. The new Secretary made these duties his own.

Under Tama Jim Wilson's guidance, the Department of Agriculture became a first-rate research institution. Before Wilson became Secretary, scientists had been working in small groups with little over-all direction except in the Bureau of Animal Industry and the Weather Bureau. Some of these groups were independent, and others were loosely attached to the divisions, scattered in several small buildings. Wilson was determined that the Department should be housed in a "monumental edifice," where the scientists would have ample space and facilities. He requested sufficient funds from Congress to build such a structure. A story still persists that President Theodore Roosevelt met Wilson one Saturday afternoon at the old Department headquarters, and that they drove stakes in the ground to indicate the size of the building they wanted. Their plans were for a building that would extend most of the way from Twelfth to Fourteenth streets in southwest Washington at the south end of the Department grounds.

As often happens, Congress cut the request by about a third and told Wilson to scale his building down accordingly. Instead, he built the east and west wings as planned (for laboratories) and left a large open space between the wings for administrative offices. The wings were completed in 1905, but the gap between them remained for almost a quarter of a century. Finally, in 1926, Congress provided the necessary funds. Construction of the central part of the building began in 1928, and it was occupied in March, 1930.

By the end of his first term in office, Secretary Wilson had decided it was time to bring the scattered units together under more centralized supervision, and by 1905 the scientific work of the Department had been consolidated into nine bureaus (animal industry, biological survey, chemistry, entomology, forestry, plant industry, soils, statistics, and weather) and one office (Office of Experiment Stations).

Bureau of Animal Industry

Research on animal diseases began in the Department of Agriculture in 1868. The following year a special appropriation of $15,000 was made to study tick fever, fowl cholera, hog cholera, and pleuropneumonia. In 1884, the Bureau of Animal Industry was officially established by act of Congress as the first bureau in the Department of Agriculture. Its primary responsibility was to find ways to control livestock diseases. The bureau made a good start by eradicating pleuropneumonia. Congress made this possible by giving the bureau authority and funds to round up all diseased and exposed animals and to pay for and slaughter them. Congress also gave the Secretary authority to regulate the interstate movement of livestock suspected of being diseased, and to inspect animals imported into the country in an effort to prevent the introduction of foreign diseases.

Two of the most notable discoveries of the bureau came rather early in its history. The first was that cattle ticks were responsible for the spread of tick fever, a discovery that had great significance for animal and human medicine. The other discovery, which led to the development of a vaccine to hold the disease in check, was that hog cholera was caused by a virus. Both discoveries are discussed in Chapter IV.

One of the early research projects was the compilation of the *Index-Catalogue of Medical and Veterinary Zoology*. This catalogue, which lists every known parasite of man and animals throughout the world, was begun in 1891, and has grown to thirty-three volumes. Regarded as the standard work of its kind by doctors and veterinarians, it is updated as new parasites are discovered and identified. It is housed in the Parasitological Laboratory, Agricultural Research Center, Beltsville, Maryland.

The catalogue is a reminder of the manner in which research on animals often benefits humans. Trichinosis, for example, is a painful and often fatal disease of man brought on by eating undercooked pork. It is caused by a microscopic parasite that is sometimes present in pork. Research in the Bureau of Animal Industry demonstrated that the parasite is killed by thorough cooking or freezing of fresh pork. Methods of curing and smoking pork used by meat packers are based upon this research and provide a wide margin of safety to consumers.

Another example of the benefits of agricultural research to man was the discovery of a simple and effective treatment for hookworms in dogs and other animals. The scientists reasoned that the same treatment would get rid of hookworms in man and took the drug tetrachloroethylene themselves to prove that it was safe. It has been used widely in the United States and throughout the world wherever hookworm is a parasite of man.

Other major research of the bureau dealt with bovine tuberculosis and brucellosis. The standard method for detecting animals infected with tuberculosis was the use of tuberculin as a diagnostic agent. The German scientist Robert Koch originally made tuberculin in 1890. Bureau scientists produced a product far superior to the original, and it proved to be the key in eradicating tuberculosis in cattle. Discovery of strain 19 vaccine likewise provided a necessary tool in eradicating brucellosis.

Animal husbandry research was strengthened in 1910 when a 475-acre farm was purchased at Beltsville, Maryland, forming the nucleus of what is now the Agricultural Research Center. Thousands of guinea pigs and other laboratory animals are kept at the farm, together with herds of cattle, sheep, and hogs, and large flocks of chickens and turkeys. Some of the basic principles of inbreeding have been worked out at Beltsville in experiments extending over many years. The Beltsville small white turkey was developed there, as were new breeds of leaner, meatier hogs.

Office of Experiment Stations

The Office of Experiment Stations was established in 1888 under authority of the Hatch Act of 1887. Although not now a part of the Agricultural Research Service, this agency was for several years a part of the Service, and has always been intimately associated with research in the Department of Agriculture. For this reason it is described here, in connection with the other scientific agencies that comprise the present Agricultural Research Service.

The mission of the Office of Experiment Stations—now the Cooperative State Research Service—was to administer the federal-grant funds provided by the Hatch Act for state agricultural experiment stations, to coordinate and give leadership to state research, and to serve as a central point for exchange of information between the states. Throughout its long history, the agency has faithfully carried out these responsibilities, always ready to champion the cause of the stations. Because of its unique character—a federal agency devoted to the interests of state experiment stations—it has played an important part in the federal-state cooperative research program.

This partnership goes a long way to explain the remarkable influence of science on American agriculture. It has no parallel in other countries and is greatly admired by agricultural visitors from abroad. The role of the Agricultural Research Service in this partnership is discussed in Chapter VII.

Bureau of Chemistry

The Bureau of Chemistry was created in 1901, when many people held high hopes for the improvement of farming through the application of science, especially chemistry. Secretary James Wilson shared these hopes and gave recognition to the chemical work of the Department by giving the Division of Chemistry bureau status.

The first chief of the bureau was Dr. Harvey W. Wiley, who became famous for his untiring efforts to give consumers more wholesome foods. It was not uncommon for processed foods to contain adulterants of various kinds or to bear labels that were misleading as to quality or content of packages. His analyses of hundreds of foods gave him evidence that could not be refuted, and he published his own improved methods of analysis for all to use. His publications became the standard works in their field and were used in colleges and universities. His competence as a scientist, his excellent sense of public relations, and the support he received from President Theodore Roosevelt were instrumental in persuading Congress to enact the so-called pure-food law in 1906. Administration of the law was assigned to the Bureau of Chemistry.

The bureau was also active in research. Improved methods of analysis were worked out for many items, including soils, fertilizers, and plant wastes. One of the most significant research jobs in the early 1900's was that done by Wiley himself on sugar beets. He studied the effects of location, climate, and other environmental factors on the growth and sugar content of beets. Because of this work, which provided a blueprint for the successful growing of sugar beets, he is often called the father of the sugar beet industry in the United States.

World War I brought new demands to all agencies of government. A wartime contribution from the Bureau of Chemistry that was especially useful was the development of a method for making synthetic dyes as good as the German products, which were no longer available. The key to this accomplishment was the discovery of an inexpensive method of making phthalic anhydride, an intermediate in the manufacture of dyes, plastics, and many other products now in daily use.

One of the aims of chemical research in the Department of Agriculture almost from the beginning was to determine the constituents of farm products in the hope that new uses might be found for these products in industry. Some of the work had direct application in industry, as illustrated by the work on dyes. Many by-products were developed from citrus fruits, and canned grapefruit and citrus juices opened up new markets for citrus growers. The biggest strike of all came many years later when frozen concentrated orange juice was developed in cooperation with the Florida Citrus Commission.

In a Department of Agriculture reorganization, effective July 1, 1927, all regulatory duties pertaining to the enforcement of the Pure Food and Drugs Act were transferred to a new Food, Drug, and Insecticide Administration within the Department. The Bureau of Chemistry thus became a research unit. When the Bureau of Soils was abolished, most of its work was transferred to the Bureau of Chemistry, which was then renamed the Bureau of Chemistry and Soils. Also transferred to the new bureau were the Divisions of Soil Fertility and Soil Bacteriology (from the Bureau of Plant Industry) and the Fixed Nitrogen Research Laboratory, which had been an independent unit.

While the rest of the country was enjoying unprecedented

prosperity in the 1920's, farmers were plagued with surplus crops and low prices. Many people thought that science could solve the surplus problem. Research had made it possible for farmers to grow the surpluses, they said; now Congress should give research a chance to discover new uses for the surpluses. Many who held this view also said that the Department should stop the price support programs and let the efficient farmers squeeze out the inefficient. This prompted Congress to order a comprehensive study to determine if an intensive research program aimed at developing new uses for farm products would be worthwhile. This study, reflecting the judgment of experts in the state experiment stations and in industry, concluded that such a research program was warranted. As a consequence, in the Agricultural Adjustment Act of 1938, Congress directed the Secretary of Agriculture

> to establish, equip and maintain four regional research laboratories, one in each major farm-producing area, and at such laboratories to conduct researches into and to develop new scientific, chemical, and technical uses and new extended markets and outlets for farm commodities and products and by-products thereof. Such research and development shall be devoted primarily to those commodities in which there are regular or seasonal surpluses.

Even before the four new laboratories were authorized, they had been anticipated in a reorganization of the bureau in October, 1938. All the soils research had been transferred to the Bureau of Plant Industry except that dealing specifically with soil erosion, which went to the Soil Conservation Service. The Bureau of Agricultural Engineering had been abolished and its functions transferred to the new Bureau of Agricultural Chemistry and Engineering. (The name of the bureau was changed again in 1943 to Bureau of Agricultural and Industrial Chemistry. This name lasted until the bureau was abolished in the reorganization of 1953 that created the Agricultural Research Service.)

The four regional laboratories were constructed at a cost of about $1 million each and began operations in 1940 at Philadelphia, Pennsylvania, Peoria, Illinois, New Orleans, Louisiana, and Albany, California. For several years the laboratories operated on annual budgets of approximately $1 million each. Programs of work for the laboratories were barely approved before the nation began preparations for war, and scarcities, rather than surpluses, became a major concern. For the duration of World War II, the new laboratories were concerned with commercial production of penicillin, sweetening agents from grains to replace sugar, synthetic rubber and rubber substitutes, dehydrated foods of all kinds for the armed forces, and treatments to make cotton resist mildew, rotting, and other hazards of military use.

Japan's surrender brought to an abrupt end many of the wartime jobs assigned to the laboratories, and energies were once more turned to new uses for surplus farm commodities. Although the United States gave away billions of dollars worth of butter, nonfat dry milk, wheat, and other foods to western Europe under the Marshall Plan, and to other countries under other plans, the surpluses remained until 1965–66, when restraints on production, exports, and gifts to needy nations did the job that research had not been able to do.

A product of research that did little to win the battle against surpluses but loomed large on the battlefields in Korea and in hospitals was the development of dextran as a blood plasma substitute or extender. Dextran, a carbohydrate whose unusual properties had been discovered in Europe, was an unstable compound that could not be stored or stockpiled for military use, but, among their large collection of microorganisms, scientists found one that produced dextran efficiently. Commercial quantities of dependable dextran were soon available to the armed forces and were credited with saving many lives in Korea. Development of commercial methods for producing penicillin was a wartime accomplishment, and is discussed in Chapter V.

The value of research on penicillin and dextran cannot be expressed in material terms, but officials of the Agricultural Research Service do not hesitate to use such terms in describing some of the other work at the laboratories over the last twenty-five years. Research on soybeans led to improved processing, which has made the soybean a major source of vegetable oil for food and industrial purposes and of high-protein meal, now a leading ingredient in livestock and poultry feed. Research on cotton created a market for at least a million bales of cotton annually by developing wash-wear cottons, and for perhaps another million bales through the development of stretch cottons, high-fashion cottons, flame-proof and rot-proof cottons, and other improvements in cotton.

Research on animal fats developed a market for the more than 600 million pounds a year of tallow and greases that were no longer needed for soap-making after synthetic detergents had replaced soap for kitchen and laundry use.

Research on frozen foods provided a foundation for the frozen-food industry in the years immediately following World War II and more recently established the importance of temperatures of 0°F. or below for maintaining the quality of frozen foods in storage. The Agricultural Research Service then assisted the industry in a campaign to stress the importance of applying this information.

Bureau of Soils

The Division of Soils was renamed the Bureau of Soils by Secretary James Wilson in 1901. The first chief of the bureau, Milton Whitney, and his assistant and successor, Curtis F. Marbut, refused to accept the views of leading soil scientists of Europe, and founded a new soil science for the United States. Their work is discussed in Chapter V.

Closely allied to research on soils has been that on fertilizers. Some of the earliest work of the Department and the state stations dealt with analysis of fertilizers and pointed to the need for laws requiring inspection of fertilizers to ensure that they contained the amount of plant foods claimed on their labels. All the states now have such laws.

American farmers were deprived of German potash when the Allied blockade of Germany, which followed the outbreak of war in Europe in 1914, completely stopped trade in this essential fertilizer ingredient. Soil scientists immediately began searching for domestic sources of potash and made hundreds of tests of potash-bearing mineral deposits, including those in the vicinity of Carlsbad, New Mexico. Various low-grade materials were used during the war, but by 1923 German potash again was available. Interest in domestic sources of potash was strong enough, however, to result in commercial development of the Carlsbad area, which has supplied most of our potash in recent years.

World War I also brought about a shortage of nitrogen fertilizer materials. Much of the nitrogen compounds used for fertilizers came from Chile in the form of sodium nitrate. This long haul was too costly and dangerous in wartime, so farmers faced the possibility of shortages of nitrogen as well as potash. Nitrogen fertilizer is necessary for sustained crop production on many U.S. soils, and the wartime need for nitrogen to increase food production and to manufacture munitions made nitrogen a top-priority item.

Chemists of the Department of Agriculture had conducted limited experiments of extracting nitrogen from the atmosphere at the Arlington Experimental Farm while the war was going on, but suitable facilities were not available until March, 1919. The National Defense Act of 1916 had provided funds to the War Department for investigations to determine the most practical method of producing nitrogen, and under this authority the Fixed Nitrogen Research Laboratory was built on the campus of American University in Washington, D.C. The staff at Arlington was transferred to the new War Department laboratory, but both laboratory and staff were transferred to the Department of Agriculture by Executive Order on July 1, 1921. Scientists at this laboratory developed a process for extracting nitrogen from the air and combining it into stable compounds that could be used for making either munitions or fertilizers. This process, with certain improvements, is still in use.

Throughout its history, the Bureau of Soils doggedly pursued the task of making soil surveys for the entire country—a task that is still going on in the Soil Conservation Service. The surveyors often found shocking erosion of the topsoil and emphasized this fact in their reports. One of the most resourceful surveyors was Hugh H. Bennett, who had seen results of erosion in Central and South America as well as in the United States.

Several workers at the state experiment stations also recognized the great losses of topsoil through erosion and were seeking ways to stop it. Investigators in Missouri concluded that soil erosion was the most important cause of soil depletion in the Corn Belt. The inherent danger to the nation was obvious to editors of farm publications and farm leaders, and to many members of Congress.

As a result Congress appropriated $160,000 in 1929 to operate ten regional erosion experiment stations for studying representative soil types and systems of farming for large areas. The stations were to find causes of soil erosion and suggest practical remedies that farmers could use. A new division, with Hugh Bennett as its head, was created in the Bureau of Chemistry and Soils to direct the work of these stations. A few years later, a Soil Erosion Service was created in the Department of the Interior, and Bennett became its director. When the service was transferred back to Agriculture as an independent agency in 1935 and renamed the Soil Conservation Service, the research stations were still an important part of the agency. They remained in the agency until 1952, when all agency research was transferred to the Agricultural Research Administration (and all soil survey work in the Agricultural Research Administration was transferred to the Soil Conservation Service).

Soils research continued in the Bureau of Chemistry and Soils until 1938, when it was transferred to the Bureau of Plant Industry (later known as the Bureau of Plant Industry, Soils, and Agricultural Engineering), where it remained until the reorganization of 1953, which abolished the scientific bureaus and created the Agricultural Research Service.

Bureau of Plant Industry

The Bureau of Plant Industry was created by Secretary of Agriculture Wilson in 1901 by consolidating a group of divisions and sections that had been operating independently and reporting to the Secretary. Some had been active for several years and already had worthwhile accomplishments to their credit, such as assembling a national herbarium and introducing the seedless navel orange from Brazil. The staff of the bureau included Beverly T. Galloway (chief), Frederick V. Coville, Erwin F. Smith, Merton B. Waite, Mark Carleton, Palemon H. Dorsett, Frank N. Meyer, David G. Fairchild, and William Orton, all of whom were to become famous.

Although Galloway was an authority on diseases of grapes and peaches, his greatest contribution to the bureau was leadership of the brilliant men on his staff. Coville became famous for his work in taxonomic botany (classification of plants) and his contributions to the national herbarium. His breeding work with blueberries led to the large varieties now available in supermarkets. He also discovered that blueberries and other members of the heath family of plants, including azaleas and rhododendrons, must have an acid soil for satisfactory growth.

Erwin Smith was a pioneer in the study of plant diseases. His work and that of his assistants proved that bacteria were responsible for many plant diseases, for which no cause had yet been discovered. At the time Waite came to the Department, pear blight was causing much trouble in the Middle West, and his first job was to learn how the disease spread so rapidly. One day he noticed that a pear tree on the Department grounds was swarming with honeybees. This led to a greenhouse experiment, which proved that bees were spreading the disease. Although Waite's work did not bring pear blight under control, it was the first proof that insects can carry plant diseases.

Although they were able scientists in other fields, Carleton, Dorsett, Meyer, and Fairchild were best known to the public as plant explorers. Carelton, a cereal agronomist, became famous for his introduction of hardy, drought-resistant wheats that could stand the rigorous climate of the Great Plains. He introduced the first durum wheat in this country, assuring future generations of ample domestic sources of macaroni and spaghetti.

Dorsett made the first trips to China and Manchuria in search of soybeans. He and his successor, William J. Morse, introduced hundreds of strains that were used by plant breeders to develop many new soybean varieties especially adapted to local areas of the United States. Meyer roamed over most of the world in search of fruits, nuts, and vegetables that might prove useful here, and sent home hundreds of lots of seeds, plants, and cuttings. He was drowned in China while on an expedition. Fairchild, the organizer and the dean of plant explorers, popularized his work in two books, *Exploring for Plants* and *The World Was My Garden*. It has been said that he did more than any other person to enrich American agriculture through plant introduction.

The early plant explorers searched primarily for new crops or hardier varieties of those already grown here. Gradually, the emphasis turned to a search for strains of plants, often from the wild, that could be used in breeding to add quality and disease resistance to our crops. Scarcely a crop is grown commercially today that has not been improved in this way. The earliest successes were rust-resistant wheat at the Minnesota Experiment Station, wilt-resistant flax at the South Dakota station, and wilt-resistant cotton, grown by William Orton, a Department of Agriculture scientist, whose work is discussed in Chapter IV.

Settlement of the arid West brought new and different problems. Farmers migrating from the eastern states had to learn how to grow crops with only a few inches of rainfall each year. The state experiment stations were helpful, but their resources were limited. Appeals to Congress resulted in funds for establishing field stations along the eastern fringe of the Great Plains to study dryland farming and other funds for reclamation projects to study irrigation farming. These stations were assigned to the Bureau of Plant Industry, which organized two units to direct the work: the Office of Dryland Agriculture and the Office of Western Irrigation Agriculture.

One of the early discoveries of the dry-farming stations was that crop yields were greater when the land was "fallowed" or kept free of all vegetation one year and cropped the next. This practice caught on quickly, as farmers could readily see its benefits. Fallowing was not new; it had been practiced in England before the invention of the cultivator at the beginning of the eighteenth century. In England, fallowing had made it possible to control weeds between the rows of crops, but it was used in the plains to conserve moisture rather than to control weeds. Long-range moisture studies showed that yields of wheat were directly related to depth of moisture in the soil at planting time. From these studies, tables were prepared to guide farmers in deciding to plant or not to plant when moisture was doubtful.

The irrigation stations were operated in cooperation with the Reclamation Service (now the Bureau of Reclamation) of the Department of the Interior. They were concerned with accumulations of salts in irrigated soils, methods and rates of applying water, and other problems of water use, as well as selection of the best crops and the best varieties for local adaptation.

One of the greatest developments in plant research—the development of hybrid corn—was well along before the Department of Agriculture became involved. The earliest work was done by two men, neither of whom apparently knew of the other's efforts: George H. Shull of the Carnegie Institution of Washington, D.C., who received most of the credit for hybrid corn, and Edward M. East of the Illinois Experiment Station, who began crossing corn the same year as Shull, 1905. Both observed hybrid vigor and saw its implications in increasing yields of corn, although they were looking for principles rather than practical results.

East moved from Illinois to Connecticut and continued his work on corn breeding, but it was Donald F. Jones of the Connecticut station who harnessed hybrid vigor and put it to work for corn growers. Single crosses were not dependable in growth habit or yield, so Jones made double-crossed hybrids by combining single crosses. His double crosses gave large increases in yields, and soon many stations were breeding hybrid corn in a cooperative program in which the Department of Agriculture participated.

The Bureau of Plant Industry led the way in improving fruits and vegetables through plant introduction and plant breeding. Commercial production of these crops led to large-scale planting in favorable areas, a situation that greatly increased opportunities for the spread of diseases. Potatoes, sweet corn, lettuce, tomatoes, and canteloupes were threatened with extinction by diseases, and all were saved by the development of disease-resistant varieties. The sugar cane industry of Louisiana and the sugar beet industry of the West were likewise threatened by diseases but were saved by disease-resistant varieties of cane and beets.

Bureau of Entomology

The Bureau of Entomology was established in 1904 by authority of that year's appropriations act for the Department of Agriculture. Its mission was to find ways to control insect pests—for fifty years one of the most acute needs of farmers. As early as 1881, the Division of Entomology, with an annual appropriation of $20,000, was making studies of cotton and sugar cane insects, scale insects of citrus and other plants, army worms, Rocky Mountain locusts, cabbage insects, and forest tree insects.

Cotton insects have always been a major concern of federal entomologists. The bollworm and cotton leaf worm apparently were here before the colonists, waiting for someone to plant a field of cotton. The boll weevil, more serious still, moved across the Rio Grande from Mexico in 1892 and began a slow but steady march through the Cotton Belt of the South. This insect brought about a revolution in cotton production. It drove the industry westward from the Atlantic seaboard, caused plant breeders to redesign the cotton plant, changed production methods, and levied a heavy tax on every cotton grower. The boll weevil is still one of the ten most costly pests of U.S. agriculture.

When the citrus industry of California was threatened by a foreign scale insect in 1888, Charles V. Riley, Chief of the Division of Entomology, sent an assistant to the native home of the insect to find and send back other insects that Riley thought might be holding the scale insect in check. This attempt, which is discussed in Chapter IV, was successful and resulted in the first large-scale introduction of an insect for biological control of another insect.

Another noteworthy activity of the period was the assembling of a collection of insects with information on their life histories and on control measures for those injurious to agriculture. The collection made it possible for the division to identify insects sent in by entomologists in the states—an identification service that has grown through the years and is now world-wide. The collection is housed in the Smithsonian Institution, which cooperates in the work of identification.

Like most of the other scientific bureaus, the Bureau of Entomology soon became involved in service and regulatory activities. These activities began in 1910, when the chief of the bureau was named member of a board responsible for enforcing the Insecticide and Fungicide Act of 1910. The act required that these preparations carry labels listing the exact amounts of ingredients and that the products must be effective against the intended pests and safe for people using them. This act has been amended several times to meet the needs of changing conditions.

Another regulatory act closely associated with the Bureau of Entomology from its beginning was the Plant Quarantine Act of 1912, designed to prevent introduction of plant pests into the United States from abroad and to prevent pests already here from spreading from state to state. The Federal Horticultural Board was created to administer the act, and its members were appointed by the Secretary of Agriculture. Charles L. Marlatt, Chief of the Bureau of Entomology, served as chairman until 1928, when the board was abolished and its functions were transferred to the new Plant Quarantine and Control Administration. The name was changed in 1932 to Bureau of Plant Quarantine, and this bureau was combined with the Bureau of Entomology in 1934 to form the Bureau of Entomology and Plant Quarantine. Marlatt was named chief of the new bureau.

In recent years, enforcement of quarantines to keep foreign insects and diseases out of the country has been much complicated by international air traffic, which began in 1927, with flights between Florida and Cuba. The next year, the Graf Zeppelin arrived from Germany with plant material infested with insects—the first recorded violation by air traffic of the foreign plant quarantine. Such violations are now intercepted by federal inspectors many times every day.

Although airplanes have added to quarantine problems, they have proved quite useful in controlling agricultural pests. The first use of an airplane to control insects was in 1918, when an insecticide was spread from an aircraft in an effort to control pink bollworms in cotton fields. In 1921, a specially fitted plane was used near Dayton, Ohio, to control insects attacking catalpa trees. A year later the Bureau of Entomology used planes to fight boll weevils in Louisiana.

Grasshoppers challenged the early entomologists and continue periodically to devour the vegetation on vast areas of range land. Improved baits and modern methods of distribution make it possible to control these pests economically with less than a pound of bait per acre, distributed by airplanes or ground equipment. From the beginning of grasshopper control, the cost has generally been shared equally by the owner of the land, the state, and the federal government.

One of the tools now used in planning the war against grasshoppers and other range insects is a survey of egg masses each fall. By knowing the number of egg masses present in a given area in the fall, entomologists can accurately predict the size of the infestation the following summer. Results of the survey are announced immediately so that ranchers, agricultural extension workers, and regulatory officials in the states can join the Agricultural Research Service in planning control operations for the following year. The grasshopper survey is part of a broad insect pest survey begun by the Bureau of Entomology in March, 1921. Through a monthly publication sent to all entomologists and other state and regulatory officials, the survey provides the latest information available on insect conditions in the United States.

As farming became more intensified, insect pests multiplied. The chief weapons available to farmers were cultural practices, such as rotation of crops, and the use of a few chemicals, such as lead arsenate. Lead arsenate was widely used on apples and other tree fruits, and there was much concern among scientists about the possible build-up of arsenic compounds in humans because of the spray residue left on raw fruit. This concern led the Department to create a new Division of Insecticides in the Bureau of Chemistry and Soils in 1927 to discover chemicals that would be effective against insects yet safe for man and other forms of life.

The division immediately began a world-wide search for plants containing highly toxic constituents that might be useful in controlling insects. The most promising was a Peruvian plant known as cube, used by natives to catch fish. A small amount of the plant thrown into the water would temporarily stun the fish at that spot and cause them to float to the surface. The toxic compound in this plant proved to be rotenone, the key ingredient in powdered derris roots, a product imported from the East Indies that showed some promise as an insecticide. For a few years rotenone was the subject of much hope and publicity. Department chemists ate quantities of it to prove that it was harmless to man, and field experiments showed that it would control several insects, including the Mexican bean beetle. Pyrethrum, a plant product from China, also proved relatively harmless to man and effective against certain insects.

A difficulty with insecticides derived from plants is their relatively high cost and limited effectiveness against the hundreds of insects that compete with man for his food, feed, and fiber crops. This was the situation until World War II, when scientists discovered the amazing powers of DDT to control many different kinds of insects. That story and its sequel are told in Chapter IX.

Bureau of Dairy Industry

The Bureau of Dairy Industry came into existence in 1924, when the Dairy Division of the Bureau of Animal Industry was raised to bureau status. The division had been created in 1895 to help farmers improve on the rule-of-thumb dairy methods handed down from father to son. The early work of the division dealt with practical problems—selecting the best breed for different sections of the country, learning the relative nutritive value of feeds commonly available, and improving the quality of butter and other dairy products. This kind of research produced useful information for dairy farmers, but the really big dividends for all consumers of dairy products came from a small group of bacteriologists working in a basement laboratory in Washington.

In the 1900's, it was an accepted fact of life that creamery butter would have a slight oily or fishy flavor. Those who objected to this could keep a cow or take a chance on buying homemade butter from farmers. In 1902, a young bacteriologist, Lore A. Rogers, became convinced that the highly acid sour cream commonly used to make butter was causing the objectionable flavors. He made small batches of butter from sweet cream and found that it kept its original quality even after long periods of cold storage.

The trade was hard to convince, however, for sour cream had been used in making butter for centuries. Cream was bought in small quantities and kept for several days before churning. The only practical way to keep the cream sweet was to pasteurize it, and that meant an added expense. The Navy helped the cause by asking the Department of Agriculture to locate supplies of butter that would keep for long periods aboard ship. Rogers used the purchasing power of the Navy to convince creamery operators that pasteurized sweet cream was the answer to the problem.

Like much research, Rogers' work had effects that extended beyond the taste of butter. Scientists in the Bureau of Animal Industry had already discovered that live tubercle bacilli were present in much of the milk and other dairy products sold throughout the country. It was also known that tuberculous cows could pass the disease on to humans who consumed raw milk and other milk products from these cows. Thus Rogers and his co-workers helped to convince the public that the only safe milk was milk that had been pasteurized. However, the man who did most to protect milk drinkers was Samuel Henry Ayers, another worker in the dairy laboratory, who cleared up a common misunderstanding about milk. The universal application of his accomplishment is discussed in Chapter V.

Other research that went far beyond the bounds of a dairy farm was that of Alice C. Evans, who established a close resemblance between the organism that causes contagious abortion in cattle and the organism responsible for undulant fever in man.

Just as the work of Rogers and Ayers gave impetus to the campaign to eradicate tuberculosis from dairy herds, the work done by Miss Evans was responsible for highlighting the need to eradicate contagious abortion (later named brucellosis) in cattle.

Early work that benefited dairy farmers included cow testing to determine which animals in a dairy herd were paying for their keep. The Babcock test, developed in 1890 by Professor Stephen M. Babcock of the University of Wisconsin, made it possible quickly and accurately to determine the butterfat content of a sample of milk. For many years the Department and the state stations used the Babcock test to promote cow testing associations and the culling of poor producers. This work, known as the Dairy Herd Improvement Plan, now includes almost one-fifth of all the dairy cows in the country. It is still supervised by the Department of Agriculture.

Of the Department's research on dairy animals, perhaps that with the most far-reaching effect was research on the proved-sire method of breeding. When this work began in 1918, purebred dairy cattle were judged at livestock shows and purchased and sold on the basis of how closely their bodies conformed to the ideal established for that breed. Agricultural colleges followed the same practice and taught the students to judge cattle by their resemblance to photographs in the textbooks.

Scientists of the Dairy Division laid out a long-time study to learn what method of breeding would result in highest returns to dairy farmers. The plan to be tested was quite simple: establish a herd at Beltsville, and use only sires that had produced at least five daughters that exceeded their mothers in milk and butterfat production. The scientists did not cull poor cows, as that would have made the results appear better than they actually were. Production per cow (without culling) steadily went up from 542 pounds of butterfat in 1920 to 720 pounds in 1955. Milk production was increased correspondingly.

When artificial insemination of livestock became practical in the 1930's, the proved sire method of breeding was ready for use by those who kept bulls and sold semen. The bureau loaned most of its proved sires to associations formed to further artificial insemination.

An experiment begun in 1939 on crossbreeding of dairy cattle aroused strenuous opposition from the breed associations and from many prominent dairy farmers, who felt that the breeds should not be deliberately mixed. The object of this experiment was to learn whether hybrid vigor could be utilized to improve dairy cattle, as it had in other species of plants and animals. After fifteen years, the bureau concluded that commercial dairymen who were not interested in a particular breed could improve the producing ability of their cows by mating them to the best proved bull available, regardless of the breed. In a recent appraisal of the crossbreeding experiments, dairy scientists concluded that, although the experiments yielded valuable information, they did not actually determine the presence or absence of hybrid vigor. Because of limited funds, the bureau did not have enough animals in the experiments to make them conclusive. Present experiments on crossbreeding are designed to provide information that will answer the question of hybrid vigor in dairy cattle.

Bureau of Home Economics

The Bureau of Home Economics was established in 1923. Human nutrition research in the Department of Agriculture, however, goes back to 1894, when $10,000 was appropriated for studies on the nutritive values of foods. The task was assigned to Dr. Wilbur O. Atwater, chief of the Office of Experiment Stations, who had pioneered in similar research at the Connecticut Experiment Station. The goals for nutrition research established by Dr. Atwater were so comprehensive that they still serve as guides.

The need for more authoritative information in home demonstration work, begun in 1914 under the Smith-Lever Act, prompted the transfer of nutrition research in 1915 to the Department's States Relations Service, where it became the nucleus of the newly created Office of Home Economics. Scarcities of some foods during World War I, and the need to make better use of those available, emphasized the importance of home economics research, and the Office of Home Economics was elevated to bureau status in the reorganization of 1923, with Dr. Louise Stanley as its first chief.

The depression of the 1930's focused public attention on the bureau. A study of low-cost but adequate diets was begun in 1930 for use in areas of drought and unemployment. As economic conditions grew worse, the work was expanded, and in 1933 the bureau issued a publication listing diets at four levels of nutritive content and cost. This and related studies by Hazel K. Stiebeling and her associates were used in planning relief programs and in estimating the total food supply required if Americans were to have adequate diets.

In 1935–37, the bureau was engaged in another historic activity, a study of consumer purchases in cooperation with the Bureau of Labor Statistics. This study revealed that a third of the people in the United States were not getting adequate food and were living in substandard housing. It was the basis for a Presidential talk that aroused the nation to the plight of a large segment of its population.

As a follow-up to its nutrition studies, the bureau in 1941 published the first simple daily nutrition guide to win national acceptance. This guide has been revised regularly and millions of copies have been distributed, especially in schools and institutions where food is served. It is among the ten most popular publications ever issued by the Department of Agriculture.

Other work by the bureau has been aimed at ways to reduce the energy used in ordinary household duties. In 1948, a step-saving kitchen was designed that aroused wide interest among homemakers, equipment manufacturers, builders, and architects. Models of the first kitchen and later versions of it have been a popular attraction to visitors at the Agricultural Research Center for many years.

In 1943, the protein chemistry research in the Department's Western Utilization Research Laboratory was transferred to the bureau, which was renamed the Bureau of Human Nutrition and Home Economics. In 1953, when the Agricultural Research Service was created, the bureau was abolished and its work continued in three branches (designated as divisions in 1957): clothing and housing, household economics, and human nutrition. The Clothing and Housing Research Division was abolished in 1966.

Although the home economics research group has always been small by Department of Agriculture standards, it would be difficult to name a group whose work has meant more to consumers. Its research, its publications, and its cooperation with educational institutions at all levels have been responsible to a large extent for the good nutritional health enjoyed by this nation.

Bureau of Agricultural Engineering

Although agricultural engineering has been a subject of research in the Department of Agriculture since 1890, the Bureau of Agricultural Engineering had the shortest life of any of the research bureaus that were eventually incorporated into the Agricultural Research Service. Agricultural engineering research had the misfortune to be transferred, reorganized, and subordinated to other disciplines more than any research activity in the Department.

The first engineering studies in the Department were on irrigation. Farmers had settled much of the fertile but arid lands of the West and, with little or no knowledge of the subject, were organizing irrigation districts. A Division of Irrigation was established in the Office of Experiment Stations in 1898 to determine the best locations for artesian wells. In the meantime the federal government had turned over to the states from the public domain large areas of swamp lands that required drainage for crop production. This stimulated research on drainage, which became an added responsibility of the Office of Experiment Stations in 1902.

In 1915, Department officials decided that the office should no longer be concerned with research, and the work on irrigation and drainage was transferred to the Department's former Office of Public Roads, which was renamed Office of Public Roads and Rural Engineering. In 1921, all work in rural engineering was incorporated into the Division of Agricultural Engineering in the recently created Bureau of Public Roads.

In the early years, many of the research bureaus of the Department did their own engineering research as the need arose. The Bureau of Animal Industry carried on research on buildings for livestock; the Bureau of Chemistry did research on the prevention of dust explosions in grain milling operations; and the Bureau of Entomology developed its own spraying and dusting equipment.

The importance of agricultural engineering research was recognized on July 1, 1931, when the Division of Agricultural Engineering was raised to bureau status. Although its funds were small compared with those of other bureaus, it was concerned with irrigation, drainage, farmland development, farm machinery, and farm structures. But the old jinx was still present. After eight years as a bureau, work in agricultural engineering was combined with that in chemistry, and the Bureau of Agricultural Chemistry and Engineering was formed. This occurred in 1939, when much of the Department's chemical research was being transferred from Washington to the four regional utilization laboratories. In such an environment, it was not surprising that agricultural engineering research had difficulty in securing appropriations. After five years the engineers found themselves moving again, this time to the Bureau of Plant Industry, which was now responsible for work on soils, and had been renamed the Bu-

reau of Plant Industry, Soils, and Agricultural Engineering—
the longest name ever given to a bureau in the Department of
Agriculture.

Much of the original laborsaving machinery used on farms
represented the work of private inventors of the mid-nineteenth
century. Today the large farm equipment companies maintain
staffs of highly trained engineers who develop most of the new
machines. The needs for public research in agricultural engineering have therefore been in other areas, where financial rewards
have not been sufficient to attract large investments for research
by industry.

An example is the work of the Department's Tillage Laboratory, at Auburn, Alabama. From research at this laboratory
manufacturers have learned about designs and materials for good
tillage machinery. Thousands of tests on all kinds of tillage im-
plements have provided data used in developing tools that do a
better job for farmers with less cost for power. Other engineering
research has been aimed at preventing loss of topsoil through
erosion. Many of the principles used in fighting soil erosion with
modern terracing techniques originated in the work of the Department's agricultural engineers. Two publications issued in
1915, reporting research on terraces and on control of gullies,
remain the standard reference works in their field.

Research Agencies Formerly in the Department of Agriculture

Several well-known agencies of the federal government originated in the Department of Agriculture, but have been transferred elsewhere. The oldest of these is the Weather Bureau. It
came to the Department as a division of the Army Signal Corps
in 1891 and remained until it was transferred to the Department
of Commerce in 1940 under Reorganization Plan No. 4.

Another research group to leave the Department began as the
Office of Road Inquiry in 1893, later becoming the Office of
Public Roads, then, in 1918, the Bureau of Public Roads. It was

transferred under Reorganization Plan No. 1 on July 1, 1939, to the Federal Works Agency, where it was renamed Public Roads Administration. Its next move was to the Department of Commerce, where it again became the Bureau of Public Roads. In 1967, it became an organizational unit of the new Department of Transportation.

Interest in birds and other wildlife led to the creation of the Division of Economic Ornithology and Mammalogy in 1886. The division grew and became the Bureau of Biological Survey in 1904. It was transferred under Reorganization Plan No. 2 on July 1, 1939, to the Department of the Interior, where it merged with the Bureau of Fisheries to become the Fish and Wildlife Service.

The present Food and Drug Administration originated in the Department of Agriculture's Bureau of Chemistry. Its regulatory activities, which began with the passage of the Pure Food and Drugs Act in 1906, became the responsibility of a separate bureau in 1927—the Food, Drug, and Insecticide Administration —which was transferred under Reorganization Plan No. 4, June 30, 1940, to the Federal Security Agency (now the U.S. Department of Health, Education, and Welfare).

II

Functions of the Agricultural Research Service

The Agricultural Research Service (ARS) was established under Memorandum 1320 of the Secretary of Agriculture, Supplement 4, November 2, 1953. The effect of this memorandum was to consolidate most of the physical, biological, chemical, and engineering research of the Department of Agriculture within a single organization. This research had been performed for the most part by the bureaus just described.

ARS conducts research relating to the production, utilization, and marketing of agricultural products. It also conducts regulatory programs that involve plant and animal quarantine enforcement, pesticides regulation, and control of diseases and pests of animals and plants. Both research and regulatory activities are carried on at numerous locations in all the states, Puerto Rico, the Virgin Islands, and a number of foreign countries. A large share of the work is performed in cooperation with the states and with public and private agencies.

Special "pioneering laboratories" conduct basic research in specific areas of the agricultural sciences. Other basic research is conducted as an integral part of the regular program of each research division in the Agricultural Research Service. The administrator and the associate administrator direct supervision of all research and regulatory activities. Activities are organized into six main areas of work, with a deputy administrator in charge of each.

1. *Farm Research.* Farm research seeks to improve methods of soil and water management; to improve field and horticultural crops and the control of crop diseases, nematodes, and weeds; to develop superior strains of beef and dairy cattle, hogs, sheep, goats, and poultry and improve animal husbandry; to control livestock diseases and pests; to develop biological, chemical, and physiological methods for controlling insects harmful to men, animals, and crops; and to develop safe and efficient uses of farm power, machines, structures, and materials.

2. *Marketing Research.* Marketing research seeks to increase the efficiency and reduce the costs of marketing agricultural commodities by means of improved marketing practices, methods, facilities, and equipment; to develop methods and instruments for identifying and measuring product quality and preventing losses from waste, spoilage, and deterioration; and to develop improved methods for preventing, controlling, or eradicating insects in stored agricultural products.

3. *Nutrition, Consumer, and Industrial-Use Research.* Nutrition and consumer-use research is concerned with the development of new knowledge about human nutrition; with nutritive values of foods; with effective consumer use of food, clothing, and textiles; and with efficient management of money, time, and other family resources. Industrial-use research is directed toward finding new and expanded uses for agricultural products. Research in the chemical, engineering, and other sciences is conducted to develop new and improved foods, feeds, drugs, fabrics, industrial chemicals, and other products from agricultural commodities.

4. *Research in Foreign Countries.* ARS administers the foreign-grant research program for the Department of Agriculture under Public Law 480 and related legislation. Grants are made to foreign governments and scientific organizations for research

on new and extended uses of U.S. agricultural commodities, and for farm, forestry, and marketing research. The Foreign Research and Technical Programs Division coordinates ARS activities in international economic, technical, and cooperative assistance and relations, including training of foreign nationals in this country in ARS subject-matter fields.

5. *Regulatory and Control Programs.* The regulatory divisions of the Service administer various laws and regulations and conduct cooperative activities in animal inspection and quarantine, plant quarantine, animal disease eradication, plant pest control, and pesticides regulation. Regulatory workers seek to prevent entry into the United States of animal and plant diseases and pests, or their transmission to other countries in U.S. exports. Special programs are designed to control or eradicate many crop and livestock diseases and pests within the United States, to assure the humane treatment of livestock during transportation, and to provide for safe and effective use of veterinary biologics and pesticidal chemicals and devices by regulating their composition and labeling and by monitoring the effects of pesticidal residues in areas of extensive chemical treatment.

6. *Management Programs.* Management divisions include those usually found in an organization the size of ARS. They are devoted to preparation of the annual budget, fiscal control, personnel management, administrative services, and management of the Agricultural Research Center at Beltsville, Maryland. Three field administrative divisions serve the ARS field offices.

The brief descriptions of the functions of the Cooperative State Research Service and the Federal Extension Service that follow will help to emphasize the close research partnership existing between the Agricultural Research Service and the state agricultural experiment stations and the close relationship between ARS research and agricultural extension work in the states and counties.

The Cooperative State Research Service administers federal-grant funds for research in agriculture, agricultural marketing, and rural life at state agricultural experiment stations in the fifty states and Puerto Rico, and for forestry research at designated state institutions. Its technical staff reviews research proposed and in progress under this program, gives leadership in planning and coordinating the research, and encourages the establishment and maintenance of cooperation among the stations. It also participates in coordinating research between the Department of Agriculture and the stations.

The Federal Extension Service is the federal part of the cooperative extension service at three levels of government—federal, state, and county. It shares in financing, planning, and carrying out extension educational programs, and acts as the educational agency of the Department of Agriculture. The cooperative service, with extension offices in nearly every county, has unparalleled facilities for providing information to the public. The Federal Extension Service has a small staff of administrative and technical people that assists state specialists in a technical and advisory capacity, working with many groups and agencies, both in and out of agriculture.

State university extension specialists are professionally trained in agriculture, home economics, youth work, and related fields. The universities also cooperate with local county governments in financing the work of county extension agents. It is these county extension workers who make the research findings of the state experiment stations and the Department available locally and help rural populations to apply the best scientific information to the improvement of farms, homes, and communities.

A glance at the activities of ARS divisions will show how much the mission of the agency has changed during the half century since the scientific bureaus were created. Fifty years ago, research was just emerging from a trial-and-error concept. With a few exceptions, research was mainly a matter of adapting old information to new situations. The chief objectives until the end of World War I were to introduce new crops, increase yields, control insects and diseases, and cut costs of production.

About 1920, more efficient marketing was recognized as a critical need of farmers and a goal for research. With the depression came large surpluses, and great emphasis was placed on new uses for farm products in industry. Better control of pests, greater use of fertilizer, and widespread adoption of improved varieties, together with improvements in agricultural machinery of all kinds, resulted in still greater yields. Political hopes for quick solutions to present problems gave way to long-range planning for utilization research.

A strong trend toward basic research, both in ARS and in the state experiment stations, developed in the 1950's. This exploration of the unknown, which now constitutes nearly one-third of the total effort of these agencies, is a far cry from what was called agricultural research a hundred years ago. But this kind of research is more likely to make discoveries that benefit all citizens and not only those engaged in agriculture.

Farm Research

The Agricultural Engineering Research Division is concerned with the application of engineering principles in the production and farm processing of agricultural products. The division's research deals with the equipment, structures, and power used in present-day agriculture.

Farm equipment research is broad in scope, ranging from new equipment and techniques for seedbed preparation to mechanized harvesting of fruits, such as pie cherries. In like manner, research on grain drying seeks to develop more effective methods and equipment for the mechanical preparation and conditioning of farm products. Research on the applications of electric energy is helping to bring automation to the farm, thereby reducing manual labor around the farmstead. Animal environmental research provides information that may be used in designing new and improved types of animal shelters. Division headquarters are located at the Plant Industry Station, Agricultural Research Center, Beltsville, Maryland.

The Animal Disease and Parasite Research Division conducts research on animal diseases and parasites affecting all classes of livestock and poultry commonly kept on U.S. farms. Its purpose is to learn as much as possible about the diseases and parasites so that practical methods may be developed for their prevention, control, or eradication.

Principal activities of this division are centered at three large laboratories and eleven small, specialized laboratories. The large installations, serving the entire country, are the Beltsville (Md.) Parasitological Laboratory, the National Animal Disease Laboratory at Ames, Iowa, and the Plum Island Animal Disease Laboratory at Greenport, Long Island, New York. Work at Ames covers all classes of livestock but is restricted to diseases already present in this country; work at Plum Island is concentrated on diseases that exist elsewhere but are not present in the United States.

Although several diseases are investigated at Plum Island, the primary objective is to learn as much as possible about foot-and-mouth disease. This disease, which affects cattle, hogs, sheep, and goats, is one of the worst animal diseases known; it has been eradicated from the United States several times by the costly procedure of slaughter and disposal of all infected and exposed animals. This country cooperated with Mexico in eradicating two outbreaks of the disease there in the late 1940's and early 1950's. Canada eradicated the disease at about the same time. After these outbreaks, Congress provided funds for the Plum Island Animal Disease Laboratory, which is located about two miles off the northeastern tip of Long Island. This island location is only one of the elaborate safeguards taken to prevent infectious disease organisms from spreading to the mainland. Headquarters of the division are at the Agricultural Research Center, Beltsville, Maryland.

The Animal Husbandry Research Division conducts research to reduce costs of producing farm animals, to provide consumers with animal products of improved quality, and to provide basic animal science information that will hasten progress toward the first two objectives.

Investigations include animal breeding and feeding, feed composition and evaluation, anatomy, physiology, and management. The division also conducts research on the quality of milk, meat, eggs, and wool, on the control of avian leukosis in poultry, on the basic metabolism in the animal body of pesticides, hormones, and other chemicals used in agricultural production, and on the effect of these chemicals on animal products. Record-of-performance programs with poultry and dairy cattle are carried on in cooperation with the states.

All phases of the division's work are supported by basic research in animal biology. Included are investigations on reproductive physiology in all species of livestock to determine causes of infertility and to increase the rate of reproduction. Other physiological investigations are concerned with the response of mammary tissue to invasion by infectious agents. One long-range study is being undertaken to describe in detail the gross and microscopic anatomy of the chicken. Research is also in progress on the metabolic role of vitamin B_{12}, unidentified nutrients in food and feed, and rumen metabolism. The division maintains pioneering laboratories for the study of population genetics, immuno-genetics, and hormone physiology. Division headquarters are at the Agricultural Research Center, Beltsville, Maryland.

The Crops Research Division conducts research to improve the efficiency of producing farm crops. These include fruits, vegetables, edible nuts, oilseeds, industrial crops, cotton and cordage fiber plants, cereals, forage legumes and grasses, sugar crops, tobacco. florist crops, woody ornamentals, trees for shade and farm windbreaks, and potential new or replacement crops.

The division's research program includes basic studies on genetics and plant breeding for resistance to diseases and improvement of quality, control of plant growth by chemical and environmental means, improved management of pastures and ranges, introduction and evaluation of new plants from foreign countries for use in plant breeding and as new or replacement crops, identification of fungi and other mycological investigations, and methods of controlling weeds and plant diseases. The division also operates the National Arboretum in the District of Columbia and manages the federal agricultural research programs in Alaska and Puerto Rico.

The division maintains pioneering research laboratories for studying plant physiology, plant hormones and growth regulators, the nature of resistance to plant diseases and plant viruses, and a plant air pollution laboratory. Headquarters of the division are located at the Plant Industry Station, Agricultural Research Center, Beltsville, Maryland.

The Entomology Research Division is responsible for research on all kinds of insects that affect human well-being, crops, and livestock. Approximately 85,000 kinds of insects are found in the United States, and 10,000 of these have an economically significant effect on man's welfare. They are man's chief competitor for food and fiber, yet some of them are essential to his existence.

The division is concerned with all insects—good and bad—that influence in any way the growing of food, feed and fiber crops, tobacco, ornamentals, and all classes of livestock. It is very much concerned, for example, with honeybees and other insects that pollinate many of our fruits and forage crops. Although the production of honey is of secondary value, it rates research attention. The division also studies flies, mosquitoes, and other insects that affect the health and comfort of man.

Although insects are a constant threat to food crops, most of them can be held in check by chemical, cultural, biological, or genetic control methods. In spite of efforts to develop alternate methods, chemicals are still the most used means of controlling insects. Because of concern over the use of chemical pesticides (discussed in Chapter IX), the division began several years ago to intensify research on biological control methods, such as the development of plant varieties resistant to insects (in cooperation with the Crops Research Division and state experiment stations), attractants and baits, the use of sterile insects for their own destruction, and other new approaches.

As a result of the shift in emphasis that began in the late 1950's, about 20 per cent of the division's research effort is now devoted to conventional chemical controls, 12 per cent to biological controls (parasites and predators), 7 per cent to plants resistant to insects, 26 per cent to sterility and other new approaches, and 35 per cent to miscellaneous entomology research such as basic biology, physiology, taxonomy, apiculture, and insect vectors of diseases.

There are two pioneering research laboratories in the division, one for insect pathology and the other for insect physiology, both at the Agricultural Research Center, Beltsville, Maryland. Division headquarters are located at the Plant Industry Station, also at Beltsville. Insect identification research is conducted in collaboration with the Smithsonian Institution in the Institution's buildings in Washington, D.C.

The Soil and Water Conservation Research Division is concerned with making the best use of our two great natural resources—soil and water. Its research is directed toward the best ways to use soil for optimum production through conservation farming, the management of water supplies for maximum benefit on farms and ranches, and the influence of soil management practices on the amount and quality of water available for use by man. The division has an arrangement with the Soil Conservation Service of the Department of Agriculture whereby field workers of the service send in at regular intervals lists of problems on which there is insufficient information. These suggestions are translated into a list of research needs, which receive a high priority as funds and manpower become available.

The division has seven branches, located in geographic regions. Each works on all aspects of the division program, which is divided into three main categories: watershed engineering research, water management research, and soil management research. The division has a pioneering research laboratory for studying mineral nutrition of plants at Beltsville, Maryland. Division headquarters are at the Plant Industry Station, Agricultural Research Center, also at Beltsville. Other national laboratories of the division are located as follows: U.S. Plant, Soil, and Nutrition Laboratory, Ithaca, New York; U.S. Sedimentation Laboratory, Oxford, Mississippi; U.S. Salinity Laboratory, Riverside, California; U.S. Water Conservation Laboratory, Phoenix, Arizona; U.S. Soils Laboratory, Beltsville, Maryland; and U.S. Hydrograph Laboratory at Beltsville, Maryland.

Marketing Research

The Market Quality Research Division seeks through research to make it possible for every grocery shopper to bring home from the supermarket foods that are as "farm fresh" as it is humanly possible to produce. This calls for an understanding of the life processes that take place in fresh fruit and vegetables, grains, meats, dairy products, and other foods, from the moment they are packed until they are served.

In carrying out its assignment, the division deals with the measurement, improvement, and protection of the quality of agricultural commodities in marketing channels. Entomological, microbiological, and physiological problems arise during storage, transportation, and distribution of farm products, and the division has scientists assigned to each of these problems as well as to the development of new methods and new devices for evaluation of quality. Much of the improvement in the quality of fresh produce in stores today may be traced to research of the Department of Agriculture and the industry.

A great deal of the work of this division is closely related to the service functions of the Department's Consumer and Marketing Service, whose divisions are responsible for standardization, inspection, and grading of agricultural commodities. The ARS Market Quality Research Division works closely with the food distribution industry, which is quick to put into effect new methods to reduce quality losses in perishable products.

Headquarters for the division and its branches are located in the Federal Center Building, Hyattsville, Maryland. The division has an Instrumentation Research Laboratory and a pioneering research laboratory for post-harvest physiology, located at the Plant Industry Station, Agricultural Research Center, Beltsville, Maryland.

The Transportation and Marketing Facilities Research Division carries on research to hold down the cost of marketing farm products. Its research covers the entire operation—structures, equipment, containers, devices, and work methods—used in transporting and marketing food from the farm. It seeks ways to improve the physical elements and handling methods involved and to increase labor productivity. In pursuing these objectives, the division studies essentially all marketing operations—assembling, preparing for market, processing, packaging, precooling, loading, transporting, unloading, storing, wholesaling, and retailing.

Some of the most spectacular work of this division is represented by the comprehensive studies of terminal marketing facilities in specific cities, made at the request of city officials. Local groups, composed of members of the trade, chambers of commerce, city officials, and others, use these studies to plan modern marketing facilities that permit more efficient handling of foods. Studies are made only when there is a clear need and when there is good reason to believe they will be used. In recent years, the division has cooperated with several major cities, including Atlanta, Philadelphia, and New York, in modernizing wholesale food markets, some of them more than 100 years old.

The division's wholesaling and retailing studies have been severely criticized on the ground that this work should be done by industry rather than by a tax-supported agency. In answer, the Department of Agriculture points out that industry research in this field is done only by the large companies and is usually not made available to the trade generally. Benefits go to the large firms, which can afford the cost. Public research of the kind done by the division is published freely so that all may benefit from its use. In 1965, an attempt was made to cut off all funds for the Wholesaling and Retailing Research Branch, but the funds were restored in conference by the House and Senate committees. Division headquarters are in the Federal Center Building, Hyattsville, Maryland.

Nutrition, Consumer, and Industrial-Use Research

The Human Nutrition Research Division studies the nutritional needs of normal people and how those needs may best be met. Its mission is to learn how individual nutrients are absorbed, transported, and metabolized, in relation to age, activity, and environmental conditions. Studies of metabolic processes and nutritional requirements in man are preceded, guided, and speeded by the results of intensive studies on laboratory animals and lower forms of life, in which a greater number of factors can be controlled and more physiological responses measured during each stage in the life cycle and during successive generations of the test animal.

Research with laboratory animals is concerned with the effects of foods and nutrients on growth, reproduction, and longevity, on the composition of blood and tissue, and on the structure and functioning of tissues at various stages of the life cycle. Chief variables under study are the kinds and amounts of dietary fats and fatty acids, proteins and amino acids, and carbohydrates.

Emphasis in research on human metabolism is on determining the quantities of nutrients required by persons of various ages when they select their own foods and when they are on controlled diets, on measuring the metabolic behavior of individuals with regard to several nutrients at the same time, and on determining the availability and utilization by man of nutrients from diets. In recent years special attention has been given to the metabolism of fat and protein.

Studies of the nutritional values of foods are based on foods from various sections of the country, representing different marketing and processing methods. These foods are analyzed both as purchased from markets and as they are customarily prepared in homes. Analyses are made for amino acids, fatty acids, minerals, and vitamins. Values for calorie, protein, and fat content are derived from analyses of the proximate composition.

Research on food properties as related to quality and use involves studies to determine the chemical composition and physical properties of raw and processed foods in order to provide basic criteria for determining the characteristics responsible for palatability and functional behavior of foods as used by consumers. Principles are established and procedures are developed for household food preparation, care, and preservation. Research is conducted with fruits, vegetables, grain and dairy products, meat, poultry, and eggs. Special studies are made with selected foods for use in the school lunch and other food distribution programs of the Department of Agriculture. Headquarters for the division are at the Agricultural Research Center, Beltsville, Maryland.

The Consumer and Food Economics Research Division conducts studies of how people spend their money for food and family living, and provides many kinds of help to assist them in making wise use of their resources. Its work falls into three general categories: food consumption and diet appraisal, tables of food composition, and family expenditures and home management practices of rural households.

Food consumption and diet appraisal studies include surveys of the kinds, amounts, and costs of food consumed by households and individuals in different population groups, surveys of how families buy and use specific foods, studies of the factors that determine food choices, and nutritional appraisals of diets and food supplies. Food budgets and dietary guides are developed and published for use in nutrition and consumer programs.

In revising and augmenting the tables of food composition, the division makes a continuous review and evaluation of the world's scientific and technical literature on the composition of foods. More than 100 journals and special reports are reviewed. For seventy-five years, the Department of Agriculture has published data on the composition of foods, each new publication reflecting advances in food analyses and in knowledge of nutritional needs. Nutrients are added to the tables as information on their presence in foods and on human requirements for them become available. Advances in the technology of preparing and marketing foods and in faster transportation are reflected in the tables.

Research on family economics and rural living involves use of surveys of the kinds, amounts, and costs of goods and services used for family living in rural households, special studies of clothing and household-textile use by families, and studies of family practices in the management of financial and other resources. (Research on housing and household equipment was discontinued in 1966, when the Division of Clothing and Housing was abolished, but research on clothing was transferred to the Consumer and Food Economics Research Division.)

The division issues two periodicals that serve as resource material for leaders in nutrition and consumer programs: The bimonthly *Nutrition Program News* is prepared for members of state nutrition committees and other nutritionists in extension work, teaching, and industry; *Family Economics Review,* a quarterly, goes to extension agents, teachers, and other professional workers in family and food economics. Division headquarters are in the Federal Center Building, Hyattsville, Maryland.

The Eastern Utilization Research and Development Division is responsible for research to develop new and expanded uses for animal products (dairy products, meats, fats, and leather) and plant products (Eastern fruits and vegetables, tobacco, and maple sap). The work is carried out by nine laboratories.

The Animal Fat Products Laboratory is concerned with the development of specific products from animal fats in the fields of plastics, lubricants, and detergents, and with exploratory research on the reactions of these fats and fatty acids and other derivatives.

The Animal Fat Properties Laboratory investigates the chemical composition and structure of animal fats and makes computer analyses of fundamental chemical and physicochemical data. It studies the molecular structure of animal fats, determines their basic physical properties, and evaluates potentially useful products made from them.

The Dairy Products Laboratory is concerned with the study of dried milk products, fluid milk concentrates, cheese and butterfat, dairy processing equipment, milk flavor and allergens in milk.

The Milk Properties Laboratory concentrates on basic studies of the composition of milk, the structure of its components, and interactions among them. Much of the work is related to the effects of processing on milk properties and deals specifically with the proteins and enzymes of milk.

The Hides and Leather Laboratory performs fundamental and applied research to develop better, more versatile, and more economical leathers. It studies the composition and chemical modification of hides and skins and various processes of hide preservation and leather manufacture. The laboratory has developed a new tanning process that produces a soft-textured perspiration-resistant leather that can be dyed uniformly. Further research is aimed at making leather that is completely washable.

The Meat Laboratory studies the low temperature growth of microorganisms, the deterioration of fats and proteins at freezer temperatures, the isolation and characterization of muscle proteins, and the composition of meat flavor.

The Plant Products Laboratory does research on fruits, vegetables, maple sap and syrup, and special plants. Basic research on Eastern vegetables and deciduous fruits includes studies of chemical composition and physical structure to learn how flavor, appearance, and nutritional value of fresh farm products can be preserved in processing. Vegetable research concentrates on potatoes and potato products.

The Tobacco Laboratory research on leaf and smoke constituents and on tobacco products is aimed at improving quality and at minimizing or eliminating any harmful biological effects that may be associated with smoking. Investigations are conducted on cigar and cigarette smoke, tobacco leaf, and leaf processing. Special cooperative research is under way at the University of Kentucky on the health-related aspects of smoking.

The Engineering and Development Laboratory mainly takes the results of the other laboratories and translates them into pilot-plant operations to ascertain facts on processing problems and costs. It also originates entirely new processes. The laboratory participated in the effort to develop a vacuum process for drying whole milk. The object was a product that tastes like milk, dissolves quickly in cold water, and keeps for at least six months at room temperature without losing its quality. Industry has adopted many of the laboratory's processes, including those for making potato flakes, for recovery and use of concentrated fruit aromas, for incorporating animal fats into feeds, and for making improved leathers.

The division maintains a pioneering research laboratory on physical biochemistry at Brandeis University, Waltham, Massachusetts. The Eastern Division headquarters are at 600 Mermaid Lane, Philadelphia, Pennsylvania.

The Northern Utilization Research and Development Division is responsible for research on new and expanded uses for corn, wheat, grain sorghum, and other cereal grains, for soybeans, flaxseed, and other oilseed crops, and for new crops. Its work is carried out in six laboratories.

The Cereal Properties Laboratory studies the composition of cereal grains and the structure of their components. It seeks to develop new reactions to modify or transform these components.

The Cereal Products Laboratory conducts research on the modification and conversion of cereal grains and their constituents into new food or industrial products. It then evaluates these products for further development in cooperation with industry. There is increasing demand from industry for products with properties different from the natural starches and flours. The laboratory is seeking to meet this demand with new industrial materials from modified flour and starch. Emphasis is given to the development of materials for paper and paper products.

The Fermentation Laboratory makes use of microorganisms to develop new industrial processes and products. Bacteria, molds, and yeasts can perform reactions that man has never learned to duplicate. This laboratory maintains the world's largest collection of industrially important microorganisms, consisting of more than 17,000 species and strains of bacteria, molds, and yeasts. The collection is famous for its role in the commercial production of penicillin during World War II and in the production of dextran, a blood plasma substitute during the Korean War. More recent emphasis is on the production through fermentation of foods, feed supplements, insecticides, plant antibiotics, organic acids, and enzymes. The laboratory provides more than 2,000 cultures each year to other research laboratories and to industry.

The Oilseed Crops Laboratory seeks new uses for soybeans and flaxseed. It studies the chemical and physical properties of the oil, protein, and other constituents of the oilseeds for clues that might lead to new processes and products. Efforts have been concentrated on improving the stability of soybean oil so that it may find wider use as a liquid oil in foods. In recent years the laboratory has also given attention to ways to make soybean products more acceptable in foreign markets, and these efforts have resulted in sharply increased exports of soybeans to Japan. Linseed oil emulsions are being studied for exterior paints and as curing and antispalling agents for concrete.

The Industrial Crops Laboratory concentrates its efforts on

plants not grown commercially in the United States. There are more than 250,000 known species of higher plants in the world, but only about 100 are produced commercially in the United States. Scientists cannot help but wonder whether somewhere in the plant world there is another species that can repeat the story of the soybean. Only a minor hay crop forty years ago, the soybean is now among the five or six top U.S. crops in cash value. Crambe, a new oilseed crop commercialized in 1965, shows unusual promise. The composition of crambe seed oil makes it suitable for a number of industrial uses that do not compete with soybean and linseed oils.

The Engineering and Development Laboratory designs, installs, and operates pilot-plant equipment to get operating information and cost data on new processes and products developed in the other laboratories. It also produces sufficient quantities of new products for evaluation by industry.

The division also has a pioneering research laboratory for microbiological chemistry, which is exploring the chemical pathways whereby microorganisms break down compounds to form the nutrients needed for their existence. Division headquarters are at 1815 North University Street, Peoria, Illinois.

The Southern Utilization Research and Development Division is responsible for research on new and expanded uses for cotton and cottonseed, citrus, peanuts, pine gum, rice, sweet potatoes, and vegetables of the southern region. The following laboratories conduct the division's research.

The Cotton Finishes Laboratory develops new chemical treatments and processes to improve cotton fiber. Its objectives are wash-wear finishes and resistance to flames, oil and grease, sunlight, fungi, and airborne acids.

The Cotton Chemical Reactions Laboratory is engaged in exploratory research on the organic chemistry of cotton cellulose, cotton's major component, and its reaction with chemical compounds.

The Cotton Mechanical Laboratory is concerned with all aspects of the mechanical processing of cotton. The laboratory does research on fiber properties and structure to improve the quality of cotton textiles, to lower processing costs, and to develop new and improved processing machinery.

The Food Crops Laboratory determines the composition of important food crops grown in the South and studies the effect of different processing methods on the yield and quality of the processed foods. Research has been concentrated largely on citrus fruits, pickles, vegetables, rice, and sweet potatoes.

The Fruits and Vegetable Products Laboratory works mainly on processed citrus and vegetable products. Citrus research seeks the causes of undesirable flavor changes that sometimes occur during processing and storage of juices and concentrates. Processing research includes development and evaluation of dehydration methods such as foam-mat, spray, vacuum, puff, and freeze drying for economical production of new products.

The Naval Stores Laboratory does research on pine gum, turpentine, and rosin and studies their major components to develop new and improved industrial chemicals. Work at this laboratory revolutionized the naval stores industry by introducing modern methods to replace the small, inefficient fire stills that had been used for centuries.

The Oilseed Crops Laboratory seeks improved processing methods and new or improved products that can be made from cottonseed and peanuts. New fat products from cottonseed oil serve as lubricants, polishing agents, and food coatings. Research on cottonseed meal is concerned with developing a product that can be fed to laying hens and hogs.

The Engineering and Development Laboratory carries on mechanical and chemical engineering research and cost analysis studies to convert laboratory discoveries into commercial products. It maintains a large pilot plant for its investigations.

The division also has two pioneering research laboratories, one devoted to plant fibers, the other to seed proteins. Headquarters for the division and most of its laboratories are at 1100 Robert E. Lee Boulevard, New Orleans, Louisiana.

The Western Utilization Research and Development Division

is responsible for research on new and expanded uses for barley, castor seed, dry beans and peas, forage crops, fruits and vegetables, poultry and eggs, rice, wheat (food and feed uses), and wool and mohair. The work is carried out in nine laboratories.

The Cereals Laboratory is concerned with food uses of wheat, western rice, and barley. Studies include basic research on the functions of flour constituents in the performance of doughs, and studies on methods for making baked products of better flavor, texture, and stability. Emphasis is on ways to make protein concentrates from cereals, including those fractions now used as feed, and on developing suitable products from these concentrates to help feed people in underdeveloped countries.

The research of the Field Crops Laboratory is directed toward better processing methods for the manufacture of new or improved feeds from forages, wheat, barley, and rice. An important aspect of this research is the preservation of unstable nutrients. The laboratory conducts similar research on castor beans and safflower seed, leading to industrial raw materials, foods and feeds from the whole seed, oil fraction, or meal fraction.

The Fruit Laboratory carries on basic studies of fruits and fruit products to determine the constituents responsible for flavor, texture, and color, and to identify and control chemical and enzymatic reactions responsible for quality changes in processing and storage. Comprehensive studies of commercial frozen foods have stressed the need to maintain low temperatures throughout the storage period. Color, flavor, and other measures of quality were well maintained when the products were stored at 0°F., but began to deteriorate when temperatures were allowed to go up to 15–20°F. even for short periods. As a result, all elements of the frozen food industry have worked together to improve equipment and handling procedures for maintaining low temperatures from producer to consumer.

The Poultry Laboratory conducts studies on the chemical and physical properties of poultry meats, eggs, and products made from their components. The results are used to develop new and improved products, including uniformly tender and flavorful meats, egg products that retain their good flavor and useful properties in bakery goods, salad dressings, and other remanufactured foods. Research is also aimed at maintaining the wholesomeness of processed poultry products by minimizing microbial contamination during processing and by destroying remaining organisms, particularly salmonellae, in all kinds of poultry products.

The Subtropical Fruit Laboratory, located in Pasadena, California, studies the chemistry of citrus oils and isolates and identifies compounds responsible for flavor in citrus and uses the results to make improved processed citrus products. Other research deals with methods to prevent browning in dates, to prevent shelled walnuts from becoming rancid, and to stabilize moisture in fruits and nuts.

The Vegetable Laboratory is primarily concerned with changes that take place during processing and storage of processed vegetables. It studies the relation of composition to color, flavor, and texture in a search for ways to improve the quality of processed products and to improve processes for making them.

The Wool and Mohair Laboratory studies the physical and chemical properties of wool and mohair fibers in an effort to make the processed fabrics more appealing and serviceable to consumers. This search has shown ways to change the fibers chemically, both internally and on the surface, to create greater resistance to shrinkage, sunlight, heat, alkalies, and bleaches. Commercial equipment is used to study every step of processing wool into worsted fabrics. This laboratory has produced wool that is highly resistant to shrinkage in home laundering and also resistant to wrinkles.

The Pharmacology Laboratory serves all four regional utilization research and development divisions. It studies the toxicity and physiological action of food additives, antibiotics, pesticides, medicinals, and other chemical compounds used in farming. The laboratory also studies minor chemical constituents that occur naturally in foods and feeds. The purpose is to provide information needed to evaluate the safety and value of chemical compounds occurring or used in agricultural products or by-products.

The Engineering and Development Laboratory designs and tests new types of equipment for processing foods, develops new methods for processing foods, and develops new products. The laboratory also studies the economic feasibility of new processes and the market potential of new products. Like similar laboratories in the other regional divisions, it produces sufficient quantities of new products for evaluation by industry.

Research in Foreign Countries

The Foreign Research and Technical Programs Division administers grants to foreign governments and institutions for research under authority of Public Law 480, the amended Agricultural Trade Development and Assistance Act of 1954. Public Law 480 provides that exports of surplus agricultural products may be paid for in local currency under certain conditions. Credits accruing to the United States from these sales may not be converted into U.S. dollars, but may be used for various approved purposes, one of which is grants to qualified institutions for research that is beneficial to agriculture both in the country where the work is done and in the United States.

The program, begun in 1958, has grown rapidly. In fiscal year 1966, grant funds totaled approximately $7.5 million. Grants have been made to many countries in Europe, including Poland and Yugoslavia, and to several countries in Asia and South America. Almost every research division in the U.S. Department of Agriculture gives technical supervision to one or more of these grants. Many of the early grants have been concluded, and the results have been published. Department officials are pleased with the quality of research done under these grants.

In the technical assistance program, the division has several responsibilities. It participates with the Agency for International

Development (AID) of the State Department and with subject-matter divisions of Agricultural Research Service in developing foreign research projects, staffed by ARS specialists, for solving problems which AID considers to be significant to progress in developing countries. The Foreign Research and Technical Programs Division receives requests for technical information, for short-term technical specialists, and for long-term technical advisers to assist AID missions and foreign ministries of agriculture. It also plans and coordinates the training programs for foreign nationals who come to the United States either for formal education or for training in special techniques.

Regulatory and Control Programs

The Plant Quarantine Division is responsible for enforcing provisions of the Plant Quarantine Act of 1912 and related legislation. The purpose of the act is to prevent the introduction of foreign plant pests into the United States and the spread of pests within this country. Plant pests are defined as insects, bacteria, fungi, viruses, snails, nematodes, and any other organisms that cause injury to plants.

In spite of all the efforts of farmers to protect their crops, plant pests exact a heavy toll every year. Damage to crops is only a part of the expense. The expense of fighting pests must also be added to the loss. Most of these losses are caused by pests from other parts of the world that were brought to this country unintentionally by the early settlers.

Plant quarantine inspectors are stationed at all major airports and seaports and at border crossings. Federal plant quarantine regulations prohibit or restrict the entry of plant pests, plants, plant products, soil, or other material that might harbor plant pests. The inspectors have authority to treat restricted imports to remove pest risk, to refuse entry, or to destroy articles entering illegally. Legal penalties are provided for willful violation of the law.

The division seeks to enforce the act with as little inconvenience as possible to the traveling public and to businesses engaged in foreign trade. It is the policy of the division that plant quarantine restrictions will not be imposed unless the U.S. Department of Agriculture has determined that importation of a plant or plant product from a specific area will constitute a pest risk.

It is common knowledge that U.S. growers often benefit materially when competition from foreign countries is eliminated by a plant quarantine regulation that prohibits importation of a plant or permits it only under conditions that discourage importers. For several years, Belgian and Dutch growers tried to get import restrictions eased on azaleas and related ornamental plants. The regulations allow such plants to be imported only if all soil has been washed from the roots. Chances for survival of plants shipped under such conditions and planted in U.S. gardens are relatively low, and only the most avid gardeners have ordered them. To overcome this difficulty, European growers used sterilized peat as a growing medium and asked for a modification of the regulation. Hearings were held, conferences of experts were called, and plant scientists were consulted. U.S. growers appealed to their representatives in Congress to continue the quarantine, making it difficult for ARS to recommend changes. Scientific opinions differ, but some ARS scientists thought privately that the use of sterilized peat removed all risks of introducing pests. At the end of 1966, after several years of debate, the regulation had still not been changed.

Although opinions differ in some cases, there is no doubt about the need for plant quarantine protection. The division estimates that there are 180 species of insects not now established in the United States that are especially destructive to crops and forest trees; if all plant pests are included, the number runs into the thousands.

The Plant Pest Control Division is responsible for suppressing or eradicating agricultural crop pests. Its activities cover five areas: survey and detection operations, cooperative control operations, regulatory programs, methods improvement, and pesticide safety and monitoring operations.

Division surveys include the cooperative economic insect survey, which provides current information on insect distribution and abundance, and surveys conducted in connection with the division's control programs. The cooperative insect survey is national in scope and depends upon the full cooperation of state agricultural agencies in all the states. In addition to general insect survey operations and special service surveys, emphasis is placed on the early detection of insects newly introduced into the United States.

Control and eradication programs include the application of pesticides by means of aircraft or ground equipment and fumigation treatments. Cultural practices, resistant varieties of crops, biological agents, and other approved methods of control that do not require conventional chemical pesticides are used and encouraged.

The goal of domestic quarantines is to prevent the spread of plant pests through the movement of commodities capable of carrying these pests over long distances in interstate commerce. The goals of the division's regulatory programs are the eradication of incipient infestations of agricultural pests already introduced into the United States, the suppression of periodical flare-ups of insects or plant diseases that cannot be controlled by individual efforts, and the prevention of spread of foreign pests that have become established in limited areas of the country.

Methods-improvement work seeks new and improved control materials, equipment, and techniques to improve the operating procedures and the safety of plant pest control programs. Field tests are conducted with promising new materials during control operations of the various programs. Efforts are made to develop and utilize lures, sterilizing agents, parasites, predators, microbial organisms, and other biological control agents.

Pesticide monitoring activities of the Plant Pest Control Division determine the effects of normal agricultural use of pesticides on the environment. Special studies are made to determine existing pesticide residue levels in soil, water, crops, livestock, and certain species of aquatic and terrestrial animal life. Accidents and incidents that involve agricultural pesticides are investigated, and educational programs are conducted to prevent or reduce such occurrences.

The Animal Health Division is responsible for preventing the introduction of foreign animal diseases and the spread of animal diseases from one state to another. It eradicates outbreaks of serious diseases when directed by Congress, keeps informed on animal disease conditions throughout the world, and cooperates with neighboring countries in the control of animal diseases that threaten U.S. livestock.

The division has the closest possible working relationship with the states. Except for the control of diseases restricted to a single state, it becomes involved in virtually all animal disease problems that arise. It has worked out a clearly worded policy of federal-state relations in the prevention, control, and eradication of animal diseases.

Prevention begins at designated ports of entry and border crossings, where inspectors enforce all regulations intended to keep foreign diseases out of this country. Animals are imported into the United States largely for breeding, slaughter, or exhibition at zoos. Breeding and slaughter animals (cattle, sheep, hogs, goats), except those from Canada and Mexico, must be kept in quarantine for thirty days at facilities approved by the Department of Agriculture. No breeding or slaughter animals may be imported from countries that have rinderpest or foot-and-mouth disease.

Because of the growing demand for zoo animals, wild ruminants and wild hogs may be imported under very strict control measures. These animals come from the wild and are exposed to many diseases not present in the United States. Elaborate precautions begin with a sixty-day quarantine at an approved facility in the country where the shipment originates. The animals must enter the United States at New York City and spend thirty days in quarantine at the Animal Quarantine Station at nearby Clifton, New Jersey. If no symptoms appear during this period, the animals may then be moved to approved zoos, where they will be under permanent supervision by the Department of Agriculture.

Animal products, such as canned meats, may be imported if they are prepared in plants that have been inspected and approved by the Department. Frozen and cured meats may be imported only from countries that are known to be free of rinderpest and foot-and-mouth disease, and whose meat inspection service has received Department approval.

Animal by-products also require supervision. Each year millions of pounds of animal by-products and related materials are brought into the United States from all over the world. These products include hides and skins, wool, hair and bristles, bones, bone meal, soluble dried blood, horns and hoofs, tankage and blood meal. Also many thousands of pounds of animal glands are imported annually for use in the preparation of pharmaceuticals such as insulin, hormones, cortisone, and products used in the treatment of nutritional deficiencies. All represent a potential risk of bringing in diseases, so all are imported under rigid controls.

Prevention of disease outbreaks is also the purpose of inspection of all animals offered for sale at all public stockyards in the United States. Inspectors look for early symptoms that might mean trouble back at the ranch. Questionable animals are placed in isolation so that they can be observed for a suitable period. If nothing develops, they are slaughtered. If a disease shows up, state and federal officials and the owner are notified so that necessary measures may begin at once.

In control programs, federal responsibility includes assistance to the states in inspections to keep abreast of animal health conditions. It also includes help in enforcing quarantines designed to prevent spread of diseases through the movement of livestock. Control programs are reexamined frequently to make certain that the most appropriate methods are being used and that expenditures are justified.

When eradication is the objective, the federal government is responsible for an over-all national plan. The Agricultural Research Service must also make a good case before the Budget Bureau and the committees of Congress to obtain the funds for federal participation, usually half the cost. Pleuropneumonia was successfully eradicated in 1892; other diseases have been eradicated on several occasions since that time. In late 1966, the division was engaged in six eradication campaigns: brucellosis (cattle and hogs), ticks (cattle along the Mexican border), hog cholera, scabies (sheep), scrapie (sheep), and tuberculosis (cattle). Two of these campaigns are discussed in Chapter IV.

One of the most recent responsibilities assigned to the Animal Health Division is enforcement of the Laboratory Animal Welfare Act of 1966, the culmination of efforts by several humane societies to prevent the theft of dogs and cats and the sale of stolen animals for laboratory use and to ensure humane treatment for animals used in research.

Regulations for enforcement, proposed by ARS in December, 1966, require that dealers in dogs and cats be licensed by the Department of Agriculture and that research facilities using these animals register with the division. Both dealers and research institutions will be required to keep records of all purchases, sales, and transportation of dogs and cats. Dealers will be required to hold animals for five business days before selling or disposing of them. Dealers and research facilities covered by the act will also be required to meet ARS standards for humane care and treatment of dogs, cats, monkeys, guinea pigs, rabbits, and hamsters.

The Pesticides Regulation Division enforces the Federal Insecticide, Fungicide, and Rodenticide Act. This act requires that every pesticide be registered with the Department of Agriculture before it may be legally shipped in interstate commerce. The purpose of the law is to protect all consumers against pesticides that are ineffective or unsafe. Registration of pesticides is the heart of this division's operation. To register a product, a manufacturer must furnish sufficient research data to support his claims that the product is effective and safe when used as directed. He must also provide directions for its use. His data must be from a reliable private or public research organization.

Applications for registration are reviewed by members of the division staff who are specialists in the area of intended use. These scientists must be satisfied that the product will be effective when used as directed. Pharmacologists then review the toxicological data to make certain that the product can be safely used as directed in the label statement. If the data show that a chemical leaves a residue, the manufacturer must request the Food and Drug Administration of the Department of Health, Education, and Welfare to set a tolerance for his product. A tolerance is the maximum amount of residue permitted on food or feed. If the Food and Drug Administration sets a tolerance, the division then requires data to show that the residue will not exceed the tolerance when the product is used as directed.

When all of the other requirements have been met, division chemists review the brand name, list of ingredients, the "caution" statements, and the net contents statement on the label. All must meet specific requirements as to legibility, clarity, and position on the label. If the product passes this final review, it is given a registration number and the manufacturer is notified.

When a product is registered and placed on the market, it must live up to all the statements used in its registration. Inspectors of the division purchase pesticides and send them to division laboratories for checking. Chemical analyses are made to see if active ingredients are present in the amounts claimed, or if adulterants are present. Laboratory or field tests are made to check effectiveness, and pharmacological tests are made to determine the adequacy of safety precautions on the label. If a product fails any of these tests, the manufacturer is notified that he must remove it from the market. If he does not do so within a reasonable time, a court order is obtained and a U.S. marshal seizes the product. If circumstances warrant, criminal action may be brought against the manufacturer or shipper.

The Veterinary Biologics Division supervises the preparation and distribution of animal vaccines, serums, and diagnostic agents used in the treatment of animal diseases and enforces the Virus-Serum-Toxin Act of 1913, which ensures the safety, purity, and potency of veterinary biologics. The law requires that manufacturers of these products be licensed by the U.S. Department of Agriculture.

The division discharges its responsibility by requiring that a manufacturer submit blueprints and descriptions of facilities, lists of scientific personnel, production methods, labels, research data, and samples of the products to be licensed. If requirements are met and a license is granted, the division continues to check on sanitation, facilities, staff, production methods, and the product. When circumstances warrant, the division may suspend or revoke a license.

The Information Division is responsible for reporting the results of all ARS activities in which the public has an interest. The division issues a monthly journal, *Agricultural Research,* which reports current research activities and regulatory programs, and prepares popular publications on all phases of ARS work. It also prepares news releases and special materials for press, radio, and television use and gives special attention to keeping the public informed on all regulatory and control programs. It provides editorial assistance on manuscripts prepared by scientists and prepares speeches, testimony, and other statements relating to ARS activities for the administrator of the Agricultural Research Service and other officials of the Department of Agriculture. The work of this division is discussed more fully in Chapter VI.

Management Programs

The Administrative Services Division formulates and carries out administrative policies. It provides policy guidance to program divisions and administrative management units responsible for carrying out administrative services and reviews the effectiveness of these activities throughout the agency. Division functions cover such areas as acquiring and disposing of land, buildings, and facilities, and construction of buildings and other structures needed by the ARS.

The Personnel Division formulates personnel management policies and develops the agency's personnel programs and procedures. Its functions cover such areas as position management and classification, organization, recruitment, training and career development, employee-management relationships, incentive awards and recognition, and employee performance and conduct.

In 1959, when James H. Starkey was director of this division, he proposed and developed a plan whereby scientists would be promoted on their merits as scientists, rather than having to wait for step-by-step promotions up the rungs of the administrative ladder. The plan was approved by the Civil Service Commission for a trial period and then approved with minor modifications for all research agencies of the federal government. The plan calls for each research worker to be evaluated by a group of scientists, who consider his qualifications for the job and his standing in his profession. It has resulted in hundreds of promotions in the ARS alone, and has doubtless operated in a similar manner in other agencies.

The Finance Division formulates policies for the financial control and management of ARS funds. It reviews the effectiveness of financial systems and procedures throughout the ARS. The division's functions cover such areas as preparation and review of financial reports, analysis of expenditure data, fund accounting, cost accounting for a capital working fund, and analysis required for long-range financial planning.

The Field Administrative Divisions, located at Hyattsville, Maryland, Minneapolis, Minnesota, and New Orleans, Louisiana, serve as field offices for carrying out administrative management functions of the ARS. Each of the three divisions has branches for administrative services, finance, and personnel and supply these services to ARS field offices within their respective regions.

The Budget Division develops budget estimates and justification statements for all ARS divisions and participates in presenting the agency's budget to the Department budget review committee, the Bureau of the Budget, and the committees of Congress. It is responsible for budgetary control, allotments, and apportionments to all ARS divisions. The division also prepares budgetary reports in response to requests from members of Congress, from farm and commodity organizations, and the press.

The Division of Operations for the Agricultural Research Center, as its name implies, is responsible for the operation and maintenance of the Agricultural Research Center at Beltsville, Maryland. The center has nearly 4,000 experimental farm animals, more than 11,000 fowl, and 3,500 small laboratory animals. The division takes care of all utilities at the center and constructs roads, bridges, and small buildings. It maintains equipment, grounds, roads, and other facilities, allots space in buildings, provides fire and police protection, and operates a mail and passenger service between the center and the South Agriculture Building in Washington, D.C.

III

Organization and Reorganization

No word in the vocabulary of a government official carries a more pleasant connotation than "organization." It connotes prestige and status, both within the government and for those outside the government who deal with federal agencies. Conversely, the term "reorganization" has an unpleasant connotation to all except those who have the power to reorganize. The Agricultural Research Service came into existence in a sweeping reorganization of the U.S. Department of Agriculture in 1953. In its effects on the scientific bureaus, this was the most drastic reorganization ever to take place in the Department. Although their work was continued, the bureaus themselves were abolished.

Probably no group of government agencies had a finer tradition of service to the American people than the scientific bureaus of the Department of Agriculture. Several had half centuries of achievement behind them, and the Bureau of Animal Industry was well on its way to the three-quarter mark. Each of the bureaus could point to notable research or regulatory accomplishments, some of which are described in Chapters IV and V.

The first rumblings of reorganization reached the bureaus when the wartime reorganization was announced on December 13, 1941. In Memorandum 960, "Organization of Department for War Effort," Secretary Claude R. Wickard reduced from seventeen to eight the number of agency heads reporting directly to the Secretary by grouping the bureaus and agencies into

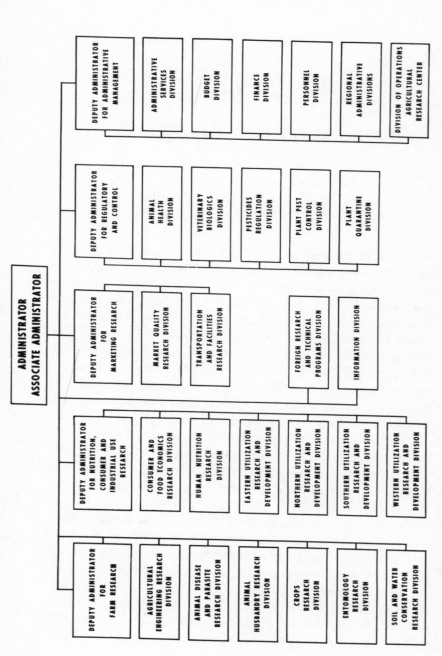

THE STRUCTURE OF THE AGRICULTURAL RESEARCH SERVICE AS OF MID-1967

administrations. One of these was the Agricultural Research Administration, headed by Dr. Eugene C. Auchter, who had been chief of the Bureau of Plant Industry. Other bureaus included in the new organization were the Bureau of Agricultural Chemistry and Engineering, the Bureau of Animal Industry, the Bureau of Dairy Industry, the Bureau of Entomology and Plant Quarantine, the Bureau of Home Economics, and the Office of Experiment Stations. The bureaus continued to operate as before, but a single administrator was responsible for their activities.

The Agricultural Research Administration

In many ways the Agricultural Research Administration was not much more than superstructure for the bureaus. The administrator had a small staff of coordinators, but until 1945 these people spent most of their time on war efforts. Originally, two were assigned to the finance office, one to personnel, and two to information coordination. The budget for the entire office of the administrator for the first year was approximately $100,000.

The administrator had authority all along to do what was done by the Secretary of Agriculture twelve years later, when he created one organization out of seven. Secretary's Memorandum 960 had listed the responsibilities of the administrator with respect to the agencies placed under his direction. He was to direct and supervise their activities and the work of their officers and employees; he was also to consolidate or integrate their administrative, technical, staff, and other services. The last item seemed to be an open invitation to consolidate all work of the bureaus, and there is good reason to believe that this was what the Secretary of Agriculture intended in his memorandum. When asked for an opinion, the solicitor of the Department replied that it was his belief that the delegation from the Secretary did contain authority to consolidate and reorganize. However, this question was not raised until the Agricultural Research Administration had been in existence almost eight years. Considering the prestige of the bureaus, the intense loyalty of their employees, and the lack of enthusiasm among many of them over the creation of the new organization, it would have required a courageous man to do in 1941 what was not done until twelve years later. The first three administrators were all past fifty years of age and had grown up for the most part in the bureaus. None of them would have relished the thought of breaking up the bureaus, even though all of them probably saw that that was the direction in which events were moving.

The speed of this move was quickened by publication of the Hoover Commission report in 1949. This bipartisan commission, headed by former President Herbert Hoover, was about as "top level" as anyone could ask. Its report commanded respect, and it was not complimentary to the Department of Agriculture. It conceded that the Department performed many useful and necessary functions, but then came to the sentence so widely quoted at the time: "It [the Department] is a loose confederation of independent bureaus and agencies."

It seems that every new administration has a compulsion to reorganize. The Eisenhower Administration of 1953 was no exception, and the Hoover Commission report supplied the inspiration. The report had recommended consolidation of all research into a research service, "divided into appropriate bureaus." It also recommended that all regulatory activities be consolidated in a regulatory service.

The separation of research and regulatory activities had been proposed before, and even attempted. In 1914 Secretary David F. Houston appointed a committee of bureau chiefs to make proposals for reorganizing the Department. Among other things, the committee recommended that research and regulatory work be separated within each bureau and that an assistant bureau chief be in charge of regulatory duties. The idea was again discussed when Henry Cantwell Wallace became secretary in 1921, and the positions of director of scientific work and director of regulatory work were established in the Appropriations Act for fiscal year 1922. Although both positions were filled, the directors served mainly as coordinating officials. Since the powers of the bureau chiefs remained virtually intact, these offices did not exert a major influence, and were later abolished.

With this record in mind, officials of the Agricultural Research Administration made a strong case for keeping research and regulatory work in a single agency. They pointed out that regulatory people looked to research for guidance in their large-scale operations and frequently sought the help of research in the solution of their problems. In addition, regulatory forces were often the first to use new research information and were in a good position to evaluate it under large-scale field conditions. (Had the administrator of the Agricultural Research Administration recommended that his organization be split down the middle—as proposed in the Hoover Commission report—it would have been a most unusual action for a government administrator.) When the new Secretary of Agriculture, Ezra Taft Benson, announced the reorganization on October 13, 1953, research and regulatory work remained together, but the scientific bureaus were abolished. What had been referred to by many as "ARA and the bureaus" was now the Agricultural Research Service.

The New Organization

Dr. Byron T. Shaw, the former administrator, was retained as administrator of the new organization. The former deputy for state experiment stations and deputy for regulatory and control work were retained, and the former bureau chiefs were appointed directors of research or regulatory work, generally in the same areas they had headed as bureau chiefs. There were directors for crops, farm and land management, home economics, livestock, utilization, and regulation and control. The fact that the former bureau chiefs were now the administrator's staff of directors meant that the heads of the former divisions could no longer be called directors because of the confusion certain to result. The

Secretary's Office had decreed that anyone who headed a division must be called director; only if a man headed a branch could he be called chief. Because of this decision, what would have been the research and regulatory divisions of ARS became branches. Elsewhere in the Department, division directors, with the same responsibilities as the chiefs of branches, were normally rated one grade higher. By 1957, when all the former bureau chiefs had retired or taken other positions, their jobs were abolished and the work was taken over by administrators. The branches were then grouped into divisions or, in the case of branches covering rather broad areas, simply became divisions. During the next several years, deputy administrators were named for farm research, home economics research, marketing research, and utilization research. Further modifications came later. Home economics was combined with utilization under a deputy administrator for nutrition, consumer, and industrial-use research. The deputy for experiment stations became deputy for research coordination when the Experiment Stations Division was made an independent agency, and the deputy for Department research coordination was transferred to the staff of the director of science and education at the time this responsibility was moved from the Agricultural Research Service to the office of the Secretary.

In the first six years of the Kennedy-Johnson Administration, the ARS gained two marketing research divisions and lost three divisions through reorganizations of other agencies. The first to go was Production Economics Research Division, which had come to the ARS in 1953. It went to the Economic Research Service when that agency was created in 1961. In the same year the Experiment Stations Division was made an independent agency and renamed the Cooperative State Experiment Station Service, later changed to Cooperative State Research Service. In 1965 the Meat Inspection Division, the largest ARS division, was transferred to the new Consumer and Marketing Service. The transfer reduced the number of employees in the ARS by approximately 3,700 and cut its appropriations by about $33 million.

Loss of the meat inspection work took from the ARS its largest segment of work devoted entirely to consumer services. Even without this large division, however, ARS people claim that a surprising proportion of their work helps consumers directly or indirectly. Since the agency deals largely with food, clothing, and other items of broad interest, it is easy to argue that its work benefits consumers as much as farmers. The Department of Agriculture has always served consumers, but this fact was not stressed nearly so much before 1961 as it has been since. For many years Department research officials were reminded at congressional hearings that their funds were for work that would benefit farmers. This made it necessary to tone down the suggestions of certain assistants, who felt it would be wise to identify the Department with the ever growing urban population. When Secretary Orville L. Freeman took office in January, 1961, he gave inspiration and courage to agency writers and officials by his own forthright public statements on consumer services. The Agricultural Research Service is the source of three-fourths of the consumer publications in the Department, and most of the "best sellers" among Department of Agriculture publications have originated in what is now the work of the Service.

ARS Administrator Shaw was far more aware of the need to identify the ARS with the urban population than any of his predecessors. He went as far in this direction as he dared, keeping in mind the opinions of the legislators on Capitol Hill who controlled the pursestrings. He changed the name of one of the divisions from Family Economics to Consumer and Food Economics Research Division. When he grouped the three small divisions that formerly made up the Bureau of Home Economics with the four large and popular utilization research laboratories, he allowed the tail to wag the dog by designating the new group Nutrition, Consumer, and Industrial-Use Research. Later he suggested to Secretary Freeman that the Department should be renamed Department of Food and Agriculture. Freeman knew this would be an unpopular proposal in Congress, but he reorganized the Agricultural Marketing Service and named it Consumer and

Marketing Service. Efforts to identify the Department and its agencies with consumers may be expected to continue unless there is a change of policy at the White House.

In 1965, Byron Shaw was succeeded as ARS administrator by George W. Irving, Jr. Irving had served several years as a deputy administrator and was associate administrator when he was promoted in 1965.

Lines of Authority

The ARS administrator, like other agency heads in the Department, reports to an assistant secretary of Agriculture. Secretary Freeman wanted an additional assistant secretary to be responsible for science and education. While waiting for congressional authorization, he created the position of director of science and education and persuaded Nyle C. Brady, head of the soils department at Cornell University, to take the job. Brady operated at the level of an assistant secretary for almost two years, until he returned to Cornell as director of the Cornell Experiment Station. Freeman then designated George L. Mehren assistant secretary in charge of marketing and consumer services, to serve also as director of science and education.

In addition to his responsibility for coordinating all research in the Department of Agriculture, the director of science and education has direct charge of the ARS, the Cooperative State Research Service, the Federal Extension Service, and the Department's National Agricultural Library. To assist in the coordinating function, he has a policy staff composed of the administrators of these agencies. He also has a full-time staff of scientists, recruited mainly from the research agencies, known as the Research Program Development and Evaluation Staff, who assist him in the over-all development of research programs within the Department. The staff coordinates research activities among Department agencies and with state, private, and other research organizations. It conducts a continuing evaluation of

Department of Agriculture research to determine if goals and needs are being met.

Because of its size and the broad scope of its activities, ARS itself has a tremendous job of coordination. A device that originated in ARS but has since been taken over by the Department's director of science and education for coordinating research is the Central Projects Office. This office serves as a control center in the review and approval of research proposals and maintains records on all Department research projects. Each new proposal must be checked against existing projects and referred for comment to all agencies doing related research. It is also referred to the Cooperative State Research Service for review in relation to research at the state experiment stations.

The Cooperative State Research Service also maintains a central project file for state research. New proposals for state research to be financed from federal grant funds must be approved by the Service in Washington. Detailed records are kept on more than 6,000 projects at state experiment stations, financed partly or entirely by federal funds. Records are kept on an even larger number of state-financed experiment station projects by means of reports voluntarily furnished by most of the state stations.

These project files provide a useful tool for coordinating research among Department of Agriculture agencies, and relating it to the total state and federal effort. Every project is considered to be new every fifth year, and receives a screening at that time. It has been said that research personnel are too busy to give sufficient attention to proposals for new projects referred to them for comment. This may be true in some cases, but officials believe the project file is the best plan so far suggested for coordinating agricultural research and that it is working satisfactorily.

Further help in planning and coordinating research comes from the research advisory committees. First there is the National Agricultural Research Advisory Committee, which concerns itself with the broad aspects of research and makes recommendations to insure coverage of all important areas in agriculture. It meets four times a year and makes its report to the Secretary.

The national committee is closely allied to the twelve commodity advisory committees, composed of leading farmers, businessmen, and agricultural scientists. Each committee meets once a year and reviews all Department of Agriculture research in its assigned fields, recommending changes agreed on at the meeting. A special staff serves as the secretariat for these committees and as liaison with the research people in the Department.

The research advisory committees have been in existence for more than twenty years, and a smooth working arrangement has developed. Each recommendation of these committees is carefully considered by the division whose work is concerned. A written report is presented at the following meeting of the committee, either stating that the recommendation has been adopted or giving reasons why it has not.

The research advisory committees were authorized by the Research and Marketing Act of 1946, one of the original purposes of which was to increase marketing research in the Department of Agriculture. By the time the bill was passed, it also contained fairly large sums for research on quality improvement and control of insects and diseases, lines of work already under investigation in several bureaus of the Agricultural Research Administration. Sponsors of the bill assumed the Secretary of Agriculture would consolidate all work on marketing, including that authorized by the new legislation, under a new agency. Instead, Secretary Charles F. Brannan named Emanuel A. Meyer as administrator of the act, with responsibility for coordinating and integrating marketing programs and policies of the Department. The effect of this was to superimpose a new administrative structure over the research bureaus. Most of these bureaus were in the Agricultural Research Administration, whose administrator, in a carefully worded memorandum, said that the problem of integrating research under the act with existing programs "was and is a matter of particular difficulty." On July 29, 1949, after

The Agricultural Research Center at Beltsville, Maryland, fifteen miles northeast of Department of Agriculture headquarters in Washington, D.C.

The Beltsville small white turkey, developed at the Agricultural Research Center. At market age, the birds weigh fifteen pounds.

Dr. Edward F. Knipling (right) being congratulated by Secretary of Agriculture Orville L. Freeman for developing the sterility method of controlling insects. This method was used to eradicate the screwworm fly in the United States.

In the screwworm "factory," trays of screwworm pupae are stacked in racks. After five and one-half days, pupae are sterilized by irradiation.

Screwworm flies are bluish-green, about twice the size of houseflies.

Boxes of sterile screwworm flies are loaded on planes and dropped over infested areas to mate with "native" flies.

An ARS scientist demonstrates the stretchability of treated cotton yarn.

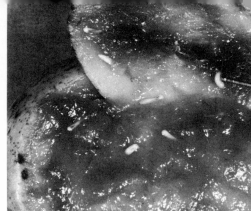

The fruit-fly larvae embedded in this intercepted mango could have started an infestation of U.S. orchards.

This orange leaf, spotted with citrus black flies, was intercepted by ARS inspectors.

ARS inspectors at Kennedy International Airport, New York, examine meats and fruits suspected of harboring pests.

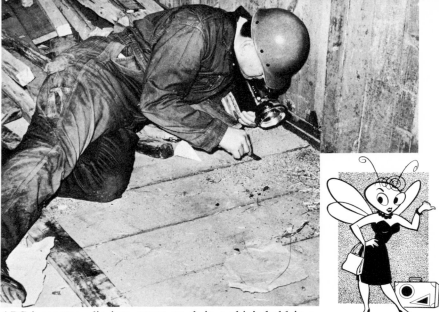

ARS inspectors dig into every crack in a ship's hold in a search for khapra beetles, a costly pest of stored grain. The hitchhiking bug symbol (inset) is used on publications and posters to remind travelers that innocent-looking fruits and plants can carry plant pests into the United States.

Simple equipment designed by the ARS can convert soybeans (top) into high-protein flour (lower right) for protein-hungry countries.

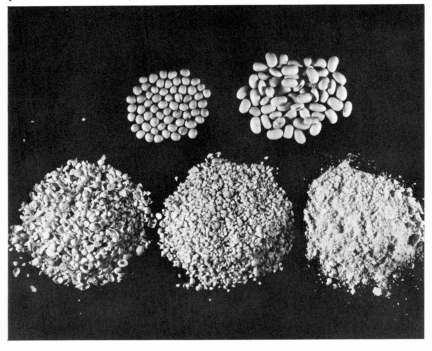

Plastic linings are used in water-conservation experiments to reduce loss of water from small reservoirs.

Azaleas blooming in the National Arboretum, Washington, D.C. The arboretum is part of the ARS.

ARS workers collect samples of water from a pond to discover whether pesticide residues are present.

Dead bees are analyzed for possible build-up of pesticide residues.

Forage crops are collected for analysis in the pesticide-monitoring program.

The Plant Industry Station at the Agricultural Research Center, Beltsville, Maryland.

Flowers (left) and fruit (center and right) of the camptotheca tree, brought to the United States by the Department of Agriculture from China in 1933. Substances from this tree show promise in arresting leukemia in human beings.

Meyer had resigned to accept a position with industry, Secretary's Memorandum No. 1237 gave the administrator of the Agricultural Research Administration full responsibility for administering the Research and Marketing Act. The funds authorized by this act were then appropriated directly to the bureaus that had been receiving allotments under the act.

The history of the research advisory committees provides an interesting sidelight on government operations. The scientists of the Agricultural Research Administration had had no experience in working with such committees, which were composed mainly of laymen. There was genuine apprehension that these laymen would not understand or appreciate the problems of research workers. There were fears that the committees might prove to be a hindrance instead of a help. And of course everyone knew that the committees would require reports—lots of them. But twenty years have brought a big change in attitude. It is doubtful if many of those now working in the Agriculture Research Service would like to do away with the committees, for they have proved to be among the most vocal supporters of ARS. By becoming a partner in the planning of research, each committee member automatically becomes a supporter, or spokesman, for the research program. There was a time when it was difficult for research officials to obtain outside support for their budget requests at congressional hearings. It is much easier now. The state experiment stations have had the same experience; they probably benefit even more from their advisory committees than does the Service.

Two other committees make recommendations concerning Department of Agriculture research—the Committee on Agricultural Science, and the Agricultural Research Planning Committee.

The Committee on Agricultural Science was established in 1962. As its name suggests, this committee has a broader base and a somewhat different objective than the other advisory committees. Its purpose is to consider the entire research program of the Department from the viewpoint of scientists who are competent to render judgments on the quality of the research. Members of this committee are all well-known scientists from a broad cross section of scientific disciplines. Of the sixteen members, half represent agencies not directly concerned with agricultural research in the U.S. Department of Agriculture and the state stations. The present membership includes the vice-president of a large state university, the vice-president for research of a large pharmaceutical concern, the assistant administrator for technical cooperation and research of the Agency for International Development, a professor of psychology, and the head of the biochemistry and nutrition department of a privately endowed university.

The Agricultural Research Planning Committee was established in 1964. Its primary functions are to assist in planning and coordinating agricultural research and to delineate areas of responsibility of federal and state agencies in this work. This committee has six members from the land-grant colleges and universities, six from the U.S. Department of Agriculture, one nominated by the National Academy of Sciences, and one nominated by the Office of Science and Technology of the Executive Office of the President. The Department's director of science and education serves as chairman. Three of the six Department members are from the Agricultural Research Service—the administrator and his deputies for farm research and consumer and industrial-use research. The other three are the administrators of the Cooperative State Research Service and the Economic Research Service, and the deputy chief for research of the Forest Service. Because ARS cooperation with the state stations represents a very large share of all Department of Agriculture cooperative research, the ARS administrator is a key member of this committee.

In carrying out his duties, the administrator has daily contacts with the director of science and education and frequent dealings with the Secretary of Agriculture. Requests for the administrator to come to the Secretary's office often result from congressional calls for urgent information or for the relaying of complaints from constituents. Because citizens are more likely to come into contact with regulatory activities than with research, a good share of these emergencies are concerned with regulatory work. Although Secretary Freeman has given a major share of his attention to such matters as farm legislation, rural areas development, and other affairs dictated by the nature of his position as a member of the President's Cabinet, he has not ignored the ARS. He has made frequent trips to the Agricultural Research Center at Beltsville, Maryland, and to the National Arboretum for special events. He has also made visits to research laboratories away from Washington and, on one occasion, took a shower and donned the white uniform required of all visitors at the screwworm "fly factory" at Mission, Texas.

The lines of authority are clear-cut below the administrator. They go from administrator to deputy, to division directors, to branch chiefs, and on down to the smallest unit. Contrary to the general belief that scientists make poor administrators because they never learn to delegate work, the two ARS administrators have been both capable scientists and capable administrators. Both knew how to delegate work and practiced it every day.

Like most large organizations, the ARS suffers from its size. Sometimes an important document may be passed down the line several times, losing a day or more in each office. When it reaches the end of the line, there is little time left to prepare the report or answer the letter. Incidentally, many people must be amazed—if they stop to think about it—at the precise information they receive in reply to a letter they have written to the Secretary of Agriculture, or even to the President of the United States. These letters are usually delegated to division directors, and many replies are models of thoroughness, even though some of them are rather long and may contain words that send the recipient scurrying to his dictionary.

The subject that consumes more of the administrator's time

than any other is money. Hardly a day passes when a question is not raised about funds for this or that project. Should he go along with Congressman X and put more money in the boll weevil laboratory, or should more go to the tobacco work at Lexington? Should he grant a division director's request for an additional $50,000 from the reserve fund? How can he present a telling argument in favor of eliminating a field station (to please the White House) when he told the appropriations committee last February that the station was vital to the livestock breeding program? How can he stretch a Budget Bureau ceiling of X million to cover urgent requests from division directors for X plus $10 million? Should he appeal the ceiling established in the Secretary's Office?

The administrator allows each deputy to run his own part of the organization. The same is true of the director for information and the director for foreign research and technical programs, who report directly to the administrator. The administrator (or the associate administrator) is nearly always available for consultation to those who report to him. Matters that can wait are held for the weekly staff meeting, attended by the administrator, the associate administrator, the deputies, and the director of the Information Division. There is free discussion at these meetings and everyone has an opportunity to ask questions and make comments. Many policy decisions are made, and agreement is reached on broad policy recommendations to be presented to the director of science and education or to the Secretary.

As in most agencies, the administrator's staff meeting triggers many other such meetings. Deputies meet with their division directors once a week to pass on important information. Most division directors hold similar meetings, but the process begins to break down at that point, because ARS personnel are so widely scattered throughout the country. In the farm research divisions, for example, at least 75 per cent of the staff is located in the field (a term used to denote any location away from headquarters). The percentage of regulatory workers located in the field is equally high.

The problems created by having such a high percentage of staff away from headquarters is dealt with somewhat differently in the two main components of the ARS. In research there is a high degree of delegation. After a project is approved, the field worker is usually given a wide degree of freedom so long as he sticks to the plan of work. This is true even at the smallest outposts, where only one or two men are employed. The purpose of visits by supervisors is to follow the progress of the work, as well as to check on what is being done.

Regulatory workers in the field are usually under closer supervision, although the amount varies in different divisions. Field forces engaged in a disease or insect eradication program are part of a highly centralized campaign that does not permit individual decisions. On the other hand, plant and animal quarantine inspectors may have rather wide latitude.

In the management divisions, there is also considerable decentralization. After several years of study, the ARS decentralized its administrative services and its fiscal and personnel work; there were four regional offices—at Philadelphia, Minneapolis, New Orleans, and Berkeley. The move was planned to give better service to the operating divisions (research and regulatory) by having management people nearby and by relieving the operating divisions of many "housekeeping" chores. At first the move was not popular with those it was intended to help, especially the research divisions. After the first year, however, most agreed the move had been wise. At the suggestion of the Budget Bureau, the work at Berkeley has since been combined with that at Minneapolis, and the eastern office has been moved to headquarters at Hyattsville.

What's in a Name?

Students of organization may wonder why some of the research divisions of the Agricultural Research Service are oriented to problems and others to scientific disciplines. This question has bothered persons outside the Service who have been asked to comment on its organizational structure. From an academic viewpoint, the question has merit. University scientists can point to their own departments, most of which bear names based upon disciplines of learning. Businessmen prefer a more forthright name that suggests what the unit is doing and why.

The fact overlooked by many is that most government agencies evolve into the kind of organizational structure, including names, that proves most practical. And what is most practical is not always the most logical. The Bureau of Plant Industry, for example, began as a group of discipline-oriented sections and divisions. Fifty years later, it consisted of several divisions, all oriented to problems.

Not too many years ago the Bureau of Animal Industry had divisions of pathology and zoology, as well as a biochemistry division. The latter was abolished, and the former are now represented by the ARS Animal Disease and Parasite Research Division. The old Division of Soil Chemistry and Physics of the 1930's would seem out of place in the problem-conscious Soil and Water Conservation Research Division of the 1960's. The name changes were made to make the work identifiable to the public it serves and (if the truth be told) to members of Congress.

But the point should not be pushed too far. The Agricultural Research Service has three farm research divisions at Beltsville whose names suggest problems and three that suggest disciplines. The administrator is not worried about this; it is a practical adjustment to environment. The forces that favor academic names, such as agricultural engineering, animal husbandry, and entomology, have so far been stronger than those favoring functional names. Perhaps the strongest forces against change are the professional societies, which naturally like to see the names of their professions used in both universities and government agencies. Forces favoring change are likely to be organized groups from agriculture and industry who benefit from research on specific commodities—and who, incidentally, are the most vocal and effective lobbyists for research funds. But the outsiders have no monopoly in this respect. Sometimes problem-oriented names are suggested by alert Department of Agriculture officials who are sensitive to the facts of life on Capitol Hill. Regardless of names, every division of the Agricultural Research Service is highly conscious of its mission, and no change in terminology would change this awareness.

One further observation may be of academic interest. The three divisions at Beltsville with academic names (Agricultural Engineering, Animal Husbandry, Entomology) receive far less than half the funds for the six Beltsville divisions. Another point that may or may not be significant is that names of the bureaus abolished in 1953 were all academic, or leaned in that direction: Agricultural and Industrial Chemistry, Animal Industry, Dairy Industry, Entomology, Home Economics, and Plant Industry. Two other bureaus (Agricultural Engineering and Soils) had previously lost their identity. The reader may draw his own conclusions but should keep in mind that such matters are subject to many influences, among which are public relations and congressional relations—the subjects of Chapters VI and VIII.

IV

Science at Work

No one can get a true picture of the Agricultural Research Service by making a list of its functions. So many of the words are unfamiliar and have a textbook ring. They fail completely to portray the life and drama of the work. Research and research-based regulatory work of the kind done in the ARS deal with vital, living things, and a surprising amount of it leads eventually to improving the welfare of people at large. For such an agency, it is not enough to describe its scientific activities the way scientists describe their work for a scientific audience. There are hundreds of stories about the work of this agency that illustrate its important role in American life.

The next two chapters relate a few of these stories, a few from research, a few from regulatory work, in the hope that they will give some idea of what this agency does.

Biological Control of Insects

The first successful introduction of one insect to control another insect took place in 1888–89 and, because of its significance in pest control, has become one of the highlights of the history of the U.S. Department of Agriculture. The event is remembered because it was a "first." It took place without approval or funds from Congress and was a big success.

The young citrus industry of California was threatened by a

scale insect. Professor Charles V. Riley, chief entomologist of the Department of Agriculture, knew that the scale was a native of Australia, but for some reason it was not a major pest of citrus trees there. He reasoned that it must have natural insect enemies that held it in check and decided to send one of his men to Australia to find and send back to California any insects that held promise of controlling the pest. Riley's first problem was to find a way to get his man to Australia.

He believed in the broadening effects of travel and had found occasion to make several trips abroad. These trips were frowned upon by certain members of Congress, who had written into his appropriation a specific prohibition against foreign travel for himself or his assistants.

But fate was kind to Riley. The Melbourne Exposition was to be held in 1889, and the State Department had received funds to send a delegation. The head of the delegation happened to be a native son of California, and Riley arranged with him to send one of his top assistants, Albert Koebele, as a member of the delegation. As soon as he arrived in Melbourne, Koebele headed for the citrus groves. He first observed that vedalia beetles (members of the ladybird family) were always present wherever the scale insects appeared. Then he discovered some of these beetles actually eating eggs of the scale insect. He knew he had found what he was looking for and began making shipments back to California. The beetles arrived in good condition and were distributed to citrus growers. They quickly became established, and the scale insect has never been a major threat to citrus trees in California since that time.

Control of Insects with Diseases

Another means of controlling insects biologically is by means of diseases that are fatal to a particular species of insect but harmless to all other forms of life. Some of the earliest agricultural writing dealt with diseases of bees. Aristotle, Virgil, and

Pliny all discussed the subject. Early entomologists observed that diseases held certain species of insects in check when weather and other conditions were favorable, and they spent much time studying these diseases in the hope of using them against the pests. Some of the most intensive work was on a disease of chinch bugs by Dr. Francis H. Snow of Kansas in the 1890's, but he was unable to produce spores of the disease in sufficient quantities to control chinch bugs under field conditions. The work was given up with the conclusion that the disease was already present in most fields, and the spores needed only the right kind of weather to multiply. When weather conditions were unfavorable, attempts to spread the disease failed because the spores could not be produced in large enough quantities.

In 1933, a survey crew in New Jersey found some abnormally white grubs of Japanese beetles, which were sent to Washington for examination. They were turned over to Dr. Gershom F. White, who had spent most of his career studying diseases of bees. By microscopic examination, he discovered that the blood of the grubs was teeming with bacterial spores and that these spores were responsible for the milky color of the grubs. Department entomologists at the Japanese Beetle Laboratory, Moorestown, New Jersey, were sure that the disease would help to control the beetles if enough spores could be produced.

Dr. Samson R. Dutky, a young bacteriologist at the laboratory, developed a technique for producing spores in commercial quantities and thus made possible the first successful large-scale use of a disease organism to control an insect pest. He inoculated grubs with the disease and after ten to twelve days prepared a spore dust by grinding the grubs and adding chalk and talc to make a fine powder. For his method of producing spores he was granted a public service patent, which he assigned to the Secretary of Agriculture. Two firms were licensed by the Secretary to make the spore dust, and quantities were prepared at the Moorestown laboratory and also at the University of Maryland.

The milky disease organism is fatal to Japanese beetle grubs but is harmless to plants, domestic animals, and people. When an area becomes fairly heavily infested with beetles, the disease dust is "planted" on top of the ground, where it multiplies very rapidly if enough grubs are present in the soil. It has been used widely in the northeastern part of the country, and is the most effective measure to control Japanese beetles.

New Concept in Insect Control

A revolutionary new idea for control of insect pests was proposed by Edward F. Knipling, a young Department of Agriculture entomologist, in 1938. Knipling's idea was to rear insects in huge quantities, sterilize them sexually, and release them in infested areas to mate with normal insects. From such matings there would be no offspring, and if enough sterile insects were released the species would breed itself out of existence. The idea seems quite practical now, but in 1938 Knipling's supervisors were not willing to risk such a novel proposal, and he had to wait until he became head of research in entomolgy in the Agricultural Research Service to give his plan a trial.

The opportunity came in 1954, after his colleagues had developed the basic techniques of the method under laboratory conditions. The real test was made with the approval of the Dutch Government on the island of Curaçao, off the coast of Venezuela, against the screwworm, a costly pest of livestock in the southern United States. The screwworm was chosen because of its monogamous mating habits. The new method completely eradicated screwworms from the small island in about six months.

Because Knipling's plan had worked so well on Curaçao, there was immediate demand from cattlemen in Florida that screwworms be eradicated from that state. Although not completely isolated from land, as was Curaçao, the state of Florida appeared to be the logical choice for a large-scale eradication effort because it is surrounded by water on three sides, and it would be possible to establish a buffer zone near the northern end of the peninsula. Winter temperatures killed the screwworm flies in areas north of Florida, and advocates of the program pointed out that if the flies were eradicated in Florida there would be no fresh supply to move up to adjoining states every spring.

Assured of state cooperation, the Department made plans to release millions of flies in Florida to give Knipling's idea a test under actual farm conditions. But flies must be reared before they can be released. The "fly factory" at Sebring, Florida, was designed to rear 50 million flies a week at peak capacity. At the beginning of the operation, low-grade horse meat and blood were used as food. Since these were to be bought by the carload, a railway siding was necessary. It takes quite a few flies to lay 50 million eggs a week, even though they are fast producers. The utmost security was required to prevent escape of the flies used for breeding. Only official visitors were permitted in the plant, and they were required to take showers and put on freshly laundered white uniforms. Upon leaving, they were required to take another shower before putting on their own clothing.

In a sense, the entire operation of the plant was like the production line of a factory. The breeding colony of flies deposited eggs in specially prepared racks. The eggs were removed and, 100,000 at a time, were placed on moist paper in a "hatchery." The tiny larvae emerging from the eggs were placed in starting trays for a day and then transferred to rearing trays of ground meat and blood. As the larvae grew and matured (in about five days), they crawled off the media into troughs, where they were collected in trays of sand to pupate. When the pupae were five and one-half days old, they were sexually sterilized by brief exposure to radioactive cobalt-60. Just before it was time for the flies to emerge, the pupae were run through a small machine that automatically discharged them into small cardboard boxes—400 to the box—to be dropped from airplanes. These flies were all sterile but not radioactive. As each box was ejected from the plane, a mechanical device opened the box so that the flies could escape and begin their search for mates. Small planes carried 1,000 boxes each.

In the early days of the Florida campaign, there was some concern among people who came across the cardboard boxes that either the flies or the boxes might be harmful. Subsequently, the boxes bore printed messages stating that neither the boxes nor the flies were radioactive and that both were harmless to man. The message also explained the reasons for dropping the flies.

The campaign that eradicated screwworms from Florida in a year and a half was much like a dress rehearsal for the main event that was to take place a few years later in Texas and the Southwest. After the success in Florida, Texas cattlemen were impatient to eradicate screwworms in their area. In addition to state agencies, many private organizations were involved, including the Southwest Animal Health Research Foundation, made up principally of cattlemen. When the Texas legislature refused to provide funds, members of this group contributed more than a million dollars to match federal funds, in order to get the campaign started in Texas. When the Secretary of Agriculture announced the beginning of the cooperative program on February 3, 1962, a supplemental budget request for $3 million had already been sent to Congress.

The "fly factory" for the Southwest was located at an abandoned Air Force base near Mission, Texas. It had double the capacity of the Florida plant and many refinements in equipment and production methods. At peak capacity, it could produce 100 million flies a week and required nearly 60 tons of ground meat, 6,000 gallons of blood, and 17,000 gallons of water. The original ARS estimate of cost had been $12 million for a three-year period. By the end of 1964, the actual cost was about $12.5 million, and the screwworm had been eradicated from the United States, except for comparatively small areas in Arizona and California not included in the original program. These states were later freed of the pest.

What had seemed an almost impossible task had been accomplished through the excellent cooperation of the livestock industry and state and federal regulatory forces. This campaign, which went much further than had been anticipated, involved high officials from the Republic of Mexico, who took the responsibility of permitting U.S. planes to fly over a large area in Mexico, dropping flies to establish a barrier zone so that screwworm flies could not come up from the south and nullify the efforts north of the border. The barrier zone must be maintained, but some officials would like to push farther south into Mexico, where the country becomes much narrower, and the zone would be less costly to maintain.

Breeding Insects Out of Existence

Few original concepts of modern science have captured the imagination of biologists throughout the world to a greater degree than Edward F. Knipling's sterility principle for eradicating insect pests. After the plan had been tested on the Caribbean island of Curaçao and had been used to eradicate the screwworm cattle pest from Florida, Knipling and his associates in the ARS turned their attention to other species of insects, including the Mediterranean fruit fly, melon fly, Mexican fruit fly, oriental fruit fly, codling moth, boll weevil, pink bollworm, European corn borer, and gypsy moth.

The success of the sterility method depends upon several conditions: (1) sexual sterility must be obtained without adversely affecting mating behavior; (2) the insects must be reared in very large numbers; (3) the sterilized insects must be released in such a way that they will come into competition with normal males; (4) if the natural population is too large it must first be reduced by other means to levels that will make it possible to adequately outnumber the natural population with sterile insects; and (5) if the sterile insects to be released are destructive, the number required to do the job must not be large enough to cause serious economic losses or create risks to human health.

Knipling has expanded his original idea to include methods that will induce continuing sterility in the natural population. Research has revealed several chemicals that produce sterility in both sexes. The most promising of these are apholate, tepa, and metepa. Use of sterilizing chemicals in combination with attractants to insure a sustained high level of sterility at a small fraction of the cost of rearing, sterilizing, and releasing is a possibility. The principal difficulty with this method, as of 1966, was insufficient information on these chemosterilants. The most promising ones belong to a group of chemicals that are active against certain types of cancer. The Agricultural Research Service is cooperating with the National Cancer Institute in studying these chemicals.

In explaining why it would be far more advantageous to sterilize insects than to kill them, Knipling likes to use the following theoretical example: If the natural population of an insect within an area is 1,000, and 900 are killed, 100 are left alive to reproduce. However, if the 900 are sterilized and continue to live and mate, they should prevent normal reproduction in 90 of every 100 fertile insects—since they outnumber the fertile insects by a ratio of 9 to 1. Therefore, only ten fertile insects can be expected to find mates that are also fertile. If some of the sterile insects should live over to the next generation, they would limit still further the ability of normal insects to reproduce. This system quickly reaches infinity, and with bisexual forms of life that means zero.

Entomologists in all parts of the world are excited about the possibilities inherent in this approach. Biologists working on vertebrate pests are also beginning to see how the sterility method could speed up their efforts. The method suggests practical ways of dealing with pests that have inflicted terrible tolls on man through the centuries. Although practical ways of using chemosterilants have not yet been developed, laboratory tests show that many species of insects and some other animals can be sterilized by this method. The list of insects includes many ancient foes of man—common housefly, mosquito, boll weevil, pink bollworm of cotton, oriental fruit fly, Mediterranean fruit fly, and German cockroach.

It would make a happy ending to the story, if we could predict that within a few years most of the major insect enemies of man will breed themselves out of existence. It has happened with screwworms, and the benefits greatly outweighed the cost. The method has been demonstrated to be effective against tropical fruit flies, which are among the worst enemies of tropical fruits. Research is moving ahead with encouraging results against codling moths, boll weevils, tsetse flies, and other major pests. But in Knipling's own words, sterilization "will not be the answer to all insect problems, but an important new weapon to use against some of our most destructive insect pests."

Fire Ant Troubles

One of the least successful of the federal-state eradication campaigns in recent years has been the imported fire ant eradication program. There are several reasons for this, some simple and others complex. The fire ant was allowed to become established over a large area in the South before the eradication campaign began. It apparently entered the country at Mobile, Alabama, and for several years spread over land that was under water part of the time or too poorly drained to have much value for farming. Entomologists knew that the fire ant was spreading and would eventually invade good farmland, but no large or vocal group demanded that it be eradicated.

Fire ants do not confine their damage to one crop or industry, as the boll weevil does, or the Mediterranean fruit fly. Fire ants do not threaten to destroy any single crop. Their honeycombed mounds up to two feet high interfere with tillage and harvesting machinery; by their fiery sting they drive workers out of fields. They are a nuisance in recreational areas, and have also been known to kill very young pigs.

The campaign against the fire ant had the misfortune to collide head on with the pesticides controversy of the late 1950's and early 1960's, which is discussed in Chapter IX. Many prominent people, who would ordinarily have taken the side of farmers and landowners, either had mental reservations about the campaign or did not wish to incur the displeasure of those who fought the program because of claims that it was harmful to fish and wildlife. Usually, when a state cooperates with the Agricultural Research Service on a control effort, it is expected that all branches of the state government will support the effort. Some of the most severe criticism of this program came from state fish and wildlife officials. Most newspapers fought the program in the name of conservation.

Many of the people in the South who influence opinion on crucial matters are dedicated sportsmen, either hunters or fishermen. Often these people live in towns or cities; to such persons, fire ants are a nuisance but not a calamity. To risk killing quail or game fish in such a cause did not make sense. Reports varied widely, and it is difficult to say to what extent other forms of life were destroyed. During the early stages of the program, when three pounds of heptachlor per acre were used against the fire ants, officials of the Alabama Fish and Game Commission charged that songbirds, game birds, rabbits, and fish were being killed. Officials of the Plant Pest Control Division do not claim that no birds or fish were killed, but that the number was insignificant and that losses were replaced by nature. This division monitors every operation, so it was one group's word against another's. Under the circumstances, it was never possible to get sustained financial support from the state legislatures to match federal funds.

With all these handicaps, it is a wonder the program survived at all. The fact that it has suggests that it must have had some value. By the end of 1966, almost 2.8 million acres had been treated in Alabama, Arkansas, Florida, Georgia, Louisiana, Mississippi, Tennessee, Texas, and the Carolinas. Most of the areas treated were at the outer edges of the infestation, to prevent further spread of the ants to new areas.

After the first two years, the amount of heptachlor was reduced to one-half pound per acre, and the opposition died down. But the damage to the program had already been done. The Methods Improvement Laboratory at Gulfport had been responsible for the reduction in the amount of heptachlor. In 1961, the same laboratory came up with a product called mirex bait, which at first appeared to be the answer to a dream: it was toxic to nothing but fire ants. The bait was corncob grits, soybean oil, and a small amount of insecticide. The scientists discovered that when an ant was attracted to one of these particles, he dutifully carried it to the nest, where all could share its lethal bounty. This seemed too good to be true, and it was.

When fire ants were later found in areas where they had been "eradicated" by the bait, the scientists made a discouraging discovery. They found that the bait had killed all stages of the ant except the eggs. This meant a reasonable degree of control, but not eradication. Experiments have shown that a second application, if timed correctly to catch the next generation before it begins to lay eggs, may still eradicate the ant. Funds were approved by Congress, and plans were being made in the summer of 1966 to mount a new attack, presumably with stronger support from the states than had been the case in earlier efforts.

Ticks Transmit Disease

Much of what man knows about himself has been learned by studies of laboratory animals. It follows that research on farm animals should likewise advance man's knowledge of himself. Results of studies in animal nutrition by the Department of Agriculture and the state experiment stations have found many applications in human nutrition—for example, the importance of minerals and vitamins in the diet. Research on animal diseases has likewise added to our knowledge of human diseases. Perhaps the best example is the research of Drs. Theobald Smith, F. L. Kilbourne, and Cooper Curtice on tick fever of cattle.

Around 1890, tick fever of cattle was causing widespread

losses. Southern cattle were often driven to northern markets, and they usually left a trail of fever along the way. Northern cattle, purchased by southern cattlemen to improve the native stock, usually contracted the disease and died. Many southern cattlemen believed that ticks were somehow responsible, because cattle that died from the disease always had ticks on them. But there was no scientific evidence to support the belief.

Theobald Smith began work on tick fever in 1888. The next year, Kilbourne and Curtice were assigned to assist him. It was a challenge, because the Department had failed in an earlier effort to find the cause of the disease. Smith and Kilbourne identified the cause as a protozoan parasite, found in the blood of infected animals. Curtice was in charge of the cattle, kept in pens at a Department farm about eight miles northwest of the Capital, near the village of Bethesda, Maryland (now the home of the famous Naval Hospital and the National Institutes of Health, and one of the world's leading capitals of medical research). In a series of experiments that were a model for their day, Smith and Curtice proved conclusively that cattle ticks were carriers of the organism responsible for tick fever.

What made their work unusual was that it was the first demonstration that a disease-producing microorganism could be transmitted by an arthropod (tick) from one animal to another. This profound discovery received world-wide recognition. The practical conclusion was clear: The way to get rid of tick fever was to get rid of cattle ticks. The Bureau of Animal Industry went to work, in cooperation with the states, to eradicate the ticks. The only treatment known at the time was to dip each animal in a preparation containing arsenic. Concrete dipping vats were built on farms all over the South. Farmers who opposed the program dynamited the vats by the thousands under cover of darkness, but the state and federal men rebuilt them as fast as they were destroyed. After many years, all the ticks were gone, and with them went a costly cattle disease.

The work was important not only because of its effect on

cattle, but because of its effect on people. The knowledge that ticks were responsible for the spread of an animal disease naturally raised the question of a similar role for insects in human disease. A few years later the mosquito was recognized as the carrier of malaria and yellow fever, thanks to the work of Dr. Walter Reed and his associates of the U.S. Army. Such is the kinship of all the sciences; their applications are unpredictable but endless.

Eradicate or Control?

Early in its history, the Department of Agriculture was compelled to make a basic decision concerning livestock diseases, which were causing heavy losses in the United States and threatened the export market for live cattle in Europe. The worst of these diseases was pleuropneumonia. It existed in several countries, but none had been able to eradicate it. Although various remedies had been tried and sick cattle were quarantined, the disease continued to spread, and England placed an embargo against all live cattle from the United States. The Bureau of Animal Industry was created to bring this and other livestock diseases under control.

Department officials decided the only way to control pleuropneumonia was to eradicate it, and Congress granted authority and funds in 1887 to purchase and slaughter all diseased and exposed animals. In a cooperative campaign with the states, the disease was eradicated in five years and has never again been a serious threat to our livestock. Authority to pay indemnities was the key to success against this disease, as it has been against many outbreaks of other livestock diseases since that time.

Foot-and-mouth disease has been eradicated several times through the slaughter of all infected and exposed animals. When two serious outbreaks occurred in Mexico in 1946 and 1953, the U.S. Department of Agriculture cooperated with the Mexican Government to stamp them out. The last outbreak in the United

States was eradicated in 1929. Foot-and-mouth disease is present in most of the major livestock-producing areas of the world except North and Central America, Australia, and New Zealand. The U.S. policy of eradicating serious livestock diseases is strongly supported by the livestock industry.

Control of Hog Cholera

For sixty years, the work of Marion Dorset in discovering the cause of hog cholera and developing a vaccine to control the disease has been cited as a historic achievement, with all the ingredients of a success story.

Young Dorset had just finished college when he came to work for the Bureau of Animal Industry in 1894. The chief of the bureau, an authority on livestock diseases, had published a paper reporting his discovery that hog cholera was caused by a bacterium, and Dorset's assignment was to find a preventive or cure. His superiors had already prepared a serum in their laboratories that they felt would be effective in controlling the disease.

In the summer of 1897, an outbreak of hog cholera in Iowa gave the young scientist a good opportunity to test the serum. He set up an experiment and injected his serum in hundreds of hogs. Most of them died of cholera, and Dorset returned to Washington, convinced that his chief was mistaken about the cause of the disease. He spent the next six years studying hog cholera, earning a degree in medicine from a local university by attending night classes. He demonstrated that the cause of the disease was an ultramicroscopic virus rather than a bacterium. He also proved that hogs that recovered from cholera were immune for life.

When the next big outbreak of cholera occurred in 1903, Marion Dorset went back to Iowa. He found that blood from immune hogs gave temporary immunity to other hogs, but the immunity lasted only a few weeks. As he watched farmers digging huge pits to bury their hogs, an idea came to him. Why not give the hogs two injections—serum from the blood of a hog that was immune and live virus from a sick hog? The idea worked, and—with several improvements—is still in use, although it frankly assumes "living with" the disease and involves losses of about $50 million a year, due to deaths and preventive vaccination costs.

It is a mark of progress that one generation is not satisfied to accept the goals, or even the brilliant achievements, of a previous generation. Dorset's work remains to this day one of the truly great achievements of agricultural research—but it was not good enough. A few countries (Canada is an example) with a much smaller hog population than ours have already proved that it is possible to eradicate hog cholera. All through the 1950's, there was agitation to eradicate this disease in the United States. Farm publications and industry leaders kept the subject alive, pointing out that Canada was spending about one-half cent for each pig marketed to keep the disease out of the country, whereas we were spending about 45 cents per pig, just to live with the disease.

State and federal officials were convinced that the disease could be eradicated, and the hog industry was calling for action. Congress provided funds, and late in 1962 a four-phase program was developed, with each phase representing a gradual build-up in the state's fight against cholera until it is eventually eradicated. As in the later phases of other eradication programs, infected herds are destroyed and owners are paid from state and federal funds appropriated for the purpose.

All states were enrolled by the middle of 1966, with nearly half of them in the final phases—and outbreaks were already showing a big drop. In the twelve-month period ending June 30, 1966, there was a total of 583 confirmed outbreaks, compared with 1,110 for the previous twelve months. In July, 1966, the incidence of the disease was at an all-time low, although not all of the large hog-producing states of the Middle West had reached their peak in the eradication phase of the program. The target date for eradication of the disease is 1972, and there is little doubt that it will be reached.

The total cost of the federal share of the hog cholera eradication program through June 30, 1966, was about $12 million. As in other joint efforts of this kind, the states match federal funds with their own, so it is correct to assume that the first three and one-half years of this program cost about $24 million, or about $7 million a year. The advantages of eradication are obvious when this figure is compared with the cost of living with the disease. When the disease is finally eradicated, hog growers will save about $50 million a year. Economic studies have shown that a large share of such savings in the costs of production are passed on to consumers.

Research Gains from Poultry Cancer

Of all ARS research, none is more fascinating than research on avian leukosis, a complex of poultry diseases that has many similarities to cancer in human beings. The research is being carried on at the Regional Poultry Research Laboratory at East Lansing, Michigan, established in 1938, when poultrymen were losing $50–$60 million annually to leukosis. One form of the disease affects the blood and is similar to leukemia in man, which makes the research at East Lansing doubly interesting.

One of the early discoveries made at the laboratory was that leukosis is linked in some way to heredity. A strain of chickens with resistance to the disease was bred at the laboratory, and another strain was bred that was susceptible to the disease. Next came the discovery that the disease is caused by a virus. Scientists now believe that a single virus, varying in potency, causes the several forms of the disease. The virus that causes the most prevalent form can be transmitted through the egg to the next generation. The disease can also be transmitted by direct contact between chickens.

One of the leads suggested by these discoveries was immunization by vaccines. Dr. Ben R. Burmester, head of the laboratory, has succeeded in vaccinating hens to make them and their offspring immune to virulent doses of the disease, but the method is too costly to become a practical control in commercial flocks. Also, immunization did not bring about the high degree of control in field tests that had been achieved under laboratory conditions. So far, the laboratory has not scored any notable victories in helping farmers eliminate leukosis from their flocks. The biggest help will probably be to breeders, who must combine all other desirable qualities with resistance to leukosis. This is a very complicated task, but Dr. Burmester thinks it can be accomplished.

The greatest victory of the regional poultry breeding laboratory may well be that it is helping medical research learn more about cancer. If it should prove to be true, as many now believe, that cancer in man is caused by a virus, the experience gained in research on leukosis should prove helpful. Researchers at East Lansing identified the avian viruses with an electron microscope and followed them from cell to cell in infected chickens. The size, shape, structure, and modes of action of avian leukosis viruses are known; this could be of great value to cancer research.

The poultry scientists found that a day-old chick can carry billions of leukosis viruses in its body and yet live out a normal life-span without developing disease symptoms.

Recently, the workers in the Agricultural Research Service helped show that one group of viruses involved in the disease lacks the protein coat that all viruses seem to need to infect chicken cells. These "defective" viruses spread by sharing the coats of other viruses that infect chicken cells. Since the coatless viruses by themselves appear noninfective, scientists wonder if the virus presumably involved in cancer in man uses a similar dodge to avoid detection.

Winning the Brucellosis Battle

Owners of beef and dairy herds have been battling brucellosis for more than thirty years, and with the help of state and federal departments of agriculture, victory is now in sight. A target date of 1972 has been set for the complete elimination of this disease from cattle. The only way to realize the extent of what has been done is to consider that every animal in every herd of cattle is a potential carrier of this disease, otherwise known as contagious (or infectious) abortion.

The drought of 1934 was the basis for starting the big campaign against brucellosis. Many farmers had been reluctant to have their cows tested, because reactors were promptly slaughtered. Even though payments were made for all animals killed, the payments reflected the low prices of the depression years. Nevertheless, farmers were badly in need of cash, the disease was gaining, and friends of farmers in Congress were looking for legitimate ways to reduce the surplus of dairy products. It seemed an ideal time to expand the brucellosis campaign.

Special funds to eliminate diseases of cattle were appropriated in 1934 and in amendments to the Agricultural Adjustment Act of 1935. The budget has carried an item every year since 1935 for the brucellosis eradication program. Since 1956, funds have averaged approximately $20 million a year. On several occasions the budget has gone to Congress with large reductions proposed, but the cuts have always been restored.

Two things explain the success of this herculean undertaking: money and organization. Congress has been liberal with money, but that alone would not have done the job. From the beginning, the brucellosis campaign has had the benefit of a smooth-working organization. State cooperation has been excellent, and support by the livestock industry has also been good. Federal and state veterinarians involved in the program are located in every state, and are regular visitors on farms. The field organization of the ARS Animal Health Division is regarded as a model for government agencies carrying on active campaign operations.

In the early years of the brucellosis program, most of the emphasis was on dairy cattle, because the disease is transmissible to man through unpasteurized milk from infected cows. As late as 1930, it was fairly common for farmers to sell small quantities of raw milk to local grocers, and very little milk consumed on farms was pasteurized. In its human form, brucellosis is best described by its older name, undulant fever. It is a serious disease, sometimes enduring a year or more.

Because of this relation to human health, dairy states along the Atlantic seaboard were among the first to join the campaign. Although cattlemen generally were not anxious to become involved in a plan that required them to pen all their animals at regular intervals for blood tests, thanks to the determined efforts of industry leaders and to liberalized indemnity payments, the campaign was making good headway by 1952 in the eastern half of the country. But the western states, with a heavy cattle population, were not in step. The program had apparently reached an impasse. It called for a blood test from each animal, and ranchers who owned large herds of semiwild cattle were not taking on the extra work of corralling all these animals for blood tests.

In 1955, the state of Washington made the first move to break the deadlock. It adopted a plan, called "market cattle testing," which requires each animal to be identified with a number at the time it leaves the ranch for market. A plastic tag containing the number identifies the ranch from which the animal came. This tag is stuck on the shoulder of each animal. When it is slaughtered, a blood sample is taken and tested for brucellosis. The tag is removed from the hide and attached to the blood sample container. If the test is positive, the owner is immediately notified. Montana tried the new plan in 1957. It worked so well in both states that it was adopted for the entire program in 1959. The plan made sense to western cattlemen, and they began to cooperate.

Perhaps there is a point worth considering here for those interested in how their government operates. Government programs tend to become rigid. In the Agricultural Research Service, the regulatory programs are soundly based upon latest research results. They have a long tradition of success, and they have the prestige of state and federal governments behind them. Yet all of this was not enough to keep the brucellosis program going. What was lacking was an idea. When it came, it was so simple that it was probably suspected by some of the hard-headed disease fighters. It took four years for the idea to become a part of the national campaign. But the main point is that it *was* adopted, and the program immediately went into high gear. Once more regulatory people proved that their campaigns must have the support of those affected. In some cases this support involves only a small part of the public. In other cases it involves the total public.

With the advent of market cattle testing, it was apparent that brucellosis was on the way out. When the campaign began, a third of the nation's herds and a tenth of all cattle were infected. By the end of 1965, less than 3 per cent of the herds and only 1 per cent of the cattle were infected.

In 1966, a still further refinement in testing was adopted. It is a new test that gives results in five minutes, and can be made right on the farm or ranch. The test requires only a few drops of blood, and the owner can watch the test being made. It will supplement, rather than replace, market cattle testing.

As the brucellosis campaign entered its final stages, the only serious obstacle was its phenomenal success. As the number of infected animals becomes smaller, the difficulty of locating them becomes greater. But every infected animal must and will be found and slaughtered. When this is done for both cattle and hogs (a swine brucellosis campaign is now in operation), farmers will save millions of dollars every year, and undulant fever will disappear.

Cows Make Their Own Protein

A study of milk cows in Finland has shown that they can lead normal lives and keep up their milk production on a diet containing no protein, the most expensive part of a cow's feed. This discovery could point the way to practical methods for producing milk in countries where little or none is now produced, because high-protein feeds cannot be grown. The research was performed by Artturi I. Virtanen, Director of the Biological Research Institute in Helsinki, with a grant from the Agricultural Research Service under Public Law 480. (Grants for research under this act have been discussed in Chapter II.)

Stomachs of cows and other ruminants have four compartments, the largest of which is the rumen. Microorganisms in the rumen convert feeds containing nitrogen to amino acids, the building blocks from which protein is made. This fact is generally known, and U.S. livestock growers normally add enough urea (a nitrogen compound) to their feeds to provide about one-third of the protein needed. Virtanen gradually replaced the normal feed of his cows with a synthetic diet of purified carbohydrates, minerals, vitamins, a small amount of corn oil, and urea and ammonia salts (as sources of nitrogen). With this diet, the cows were able to manufacture their own protein without losing weight or reducing milk production.

Earlier ARS experiments had shown that beef cows could grow normally and produce normal calves on a diet similar to that used by Virtanen, but he was the first to show that dairy cows, with their greater need for protein, could also provide their needs with low-cost urea instead of high-cost protein feeds. The research in Finland was reported in 1966. Since that time, a long-range experiment at the Beltsville, Maryland, Agricultural Research Center has revealed that, without protein feed, a cow can lead a normal life and produce a normal calf. For some reason, not yet understood, the growth rate of heifers fed the synthetic diet is about 20 per cent less than that of heifers on normal rations. Bull calves also grow more slowly on synthetic diets for the first year, but then catch up with those on normal feed. If further research shows that the feeding of urea and other nitrogen compounds is practical as a replacement for all protein feeds under farm conditions, it could drastically change feeding practices and lower the cost of feeding both dairy and beef cattle.

Breeding Plants to Resist Disease

Much of the early work of agricultural scientists with crop plants emphasized ways to improve yields. One of the greatest threats to yields was plant diseases, and both the U.S. Department of Agriculture and the states sought ways to control these diseases. A historic breakthrough in this work occurred in South Carolina during the first years of this century.

When William A. Orton, a young plant pathologist from Maine, went to work for the Department in 1899, he probably had never seen a field of cotton. His first assignment was to do something that had never been done before—develop a variety of cotton with resistance to disease. Selection of seed from superior plants had been practiced for centuries, but the earliest record of systematic selection for resistance to disease went back no further than 1895. The work was done by E. L. Rivers, owner of a plantation on James Island, near Charleston, South Carolina, in an effort to develop a strain of cotton resistant to wilt, a soil-borne disease.

Rivers was unable to combine disease resistance with yield and quality. In 1899, he called on the Department of Agriculture for help, and young Dr. Orton was sent. Together, these men made history by deliberately planting selected seed on wilt-infested soil and saving plants that survived. Several new cotton varieties were eventually developed.

While this work was going on in South Carolina, a similar story was unfolding at the experiment station in North Dakota with flax, also beset by wilt disease. In both cases the principle of survival of the fittest was applied by scientists, a principle now widely used in all crop improvement work.

Man Against Nature

For many years, wheat breeders in this country and elsewhere were baffled by a mystery: The new varieties they developed to resist the stem rust disease would stand up against severe epidemics for a few years and then suddenly appear to lose all resistance. The result would be a crop failure. Stem rust was a constant threat to farmers of the Plains, the breadbasket of the country.

The first break came when Swedish scientists reported that stem rust on wheat was not caused by the same organism that caused stem rust on oats or rye. A young plant pathologist working on a cooperative project with the U.S. Department of Agriculture at the University of Minnesota, Elvin C. Stakman, confirmed that the results reported in Sweden also applied to the rust disease in the United States. This gave him an idea for further research, which explained the mystery.

In 1913, he published results of experiments showing that stem rust on wheat is not produced by a single organism, as everyone had assumed, but by many closely related organisms, which he called pathogenic races. This discovery was the key to understanding stem rust and provided a blueprint for plant breeders to follow. It explained why the new varieties would produce good yields for a few years and then succumb. When one of these new varieties was introduced to an area, the race of stem rust that had been doing the damage would disappear, but a new race would multiply sufficiently in a few years to cause great damage.

With this solid foundation of knowledge to build upon, wheat breeders in other states and in the Department of Agriculture were able to combine into a new variety resistance against several of the most prevalent races of the disease instead of just one. But there was still another challenge to be met. They knew that new races were appearing, but where were they coming from? The answer reveals how big a task the scientists had undertaken.

Scientists had known for many years that the stem rust organism spent part of its life on barberry plants, and millions of these grew wild in most areas where wheat was grown. Spores of the disease organism developed on barberries and were scattered by the wind. When a spore lodged on a wheat plant, it began its life cycle anew. Campaigns to get rid of all barberries by digging, and later by herbicides, were only partially successful because of the great abundance of the plants. Breeding rust-resistant varieties of wheat and other small grains seemed a more practical answer, but the appearance of new races of rust made that a difficult job. Scientists eventually discovered that the new races were a result of the disease spores hybridizing in nature during the period spent on the barberry bushes. Thus, while man is busily hybridizing wheat plants to get ahead of the rust disease, nature is leisurely hybridizing the disease itself.

Harnessing Hybrid Vigor

One of the keys to the increased productivity of American agriculture since World War II is hybrid vigor, as it has been harnessed by agricultural scientists. Hybrid corn came just in time to give a big boost to feed and food production in World War II. Hybrid sugar beets and onions increased yields substantially, and hybrid sorghums gave such large increases in yields that prices were depressed for several years. Throughout this period of scientific success and economic misfortune for farmers, wheat breeders dreamed of the day when they could produce hybrid wheat.

Hybrid vigor comes from crossing unrelated strains that have usually undergone several years of inbreeding to fix the desired characteristics. The term hybrid is often used to denote any plant that is a result of planned cross-pollination of plants that are unlike genetically, but such plants may or may not show hybrid vigor. In the last thirty years, wheat breeders have developed many fine new varieties with resistance to rust and other diseases, but these are not hybrids in the true sense, as they represent several generations of selection.

One of the requirements in developing a true hybrid is a line of breeding material that is male sterile. In such plants, the pollen-bearing parts are so poorly developed—an inherited condition—that they do not function. To produce seed on male-sterile plants, the flowers must be pollinated by hand, or the male-sterile plants must be planted near the plants with which they are to be crossed so that pollen can be blown to them by winds. Neither method is practical for wheat under field conditions.

The break came in 1962, when a team from the Agricultural Research Service and the Nebraska Experiment Station and another group in Kansas simultaneously discovered a breeding line that could restore fertility to male-sterile plants. This opened up the possibility of using male-sterile lines to fix desired characteristics—just as inbreeding is used for corn—and then crossing one of the lines with the fertility-restoring line. The resulting wheat has perfect flowers that produce a crop of grain in a farmer's field.

Before a new variety of wheat is introduced, it must demonstrate that it is hardy, disease-resistant, and capable of good yields. It must also make good bread. Collectively, these are known as agronomic and milling qualities. Developing a hybrid wheat with all the agronomic and milling qualities demanded today will not be simple or quick. However, this difficulty will not stop the men who now have the tool they had awaited so long. Hybrids increased corn yields as much as 25 per cent, and there is no reason to believe that hybrids will not do the same for wheat. Perhaps hybrid rice for the hungry people of the Orient will be next on the list.

World Bank of Germ Plasm

When a plant breeder begins work to develop a disease-resistant variety of wheat or other crop, one of the first places he looks for qualities that he would like to incorporate in the new variety is the world seed collection. This collection comprises several collections that have been built up over almost three-quarters of a century by state and federal plant explorers, and are often referred to collectively as a world bank of germ plasm.

The earliest plant explorers went out in search of varieties or strains of crops that would give greater yields or be more dependable than the varieties farmers were then growing, and this effort was remarkably successful. The scientists soon realized, however, that the greatest opportunity to improve our agriculture was to search out and send back strains of plants that could be used in breeding new varieties. This meant going to the native home of the plant and collecting some of its "wild" relatives, on the theory that strains that had persisted for centuries without the aid of man must have some exceptional qualities.

The new practice resulted in piling up large quantities of seed, creating a problem of identification and storage. Each lot was numbered as it arrived, but many were sent to field stations in the states for trial and lost their identity. Also, as the collections grew, the job of "keeping them alive" required more and more effort. Although many seeds have a long life, others remain viable (alive) only a few years, and new seed crops must be grown frequently or the strains will become extinct. A further difficulty was that the collections were scattered. Some were in Washington, some at Department field stations, and others at the state experiment stations.

A permanent home for this unique world collection of germ plasm was completed at Fort Collins, Colorado, in 1958. It is known as the National Seed Storage Laboratory, and is located on the campus of Colorado State University. It provides ideal storage conditions, including a dry, cool atmosphere that can be kept at desired levels. The laboratory also has the responsibility for renewing the viable seed supply as required. This facility is strictly for long-term storage of valuable germ plasm and is not a distributing center to plant breeders, except as a last resort when working stock cannot be located elsewhere.

Four regional plant introduction stations first receive most newly introduced seeds or plants and increase these sufficiently for the needs of domestic plant breeders. On occasion, they may also be called upon to distribute seed to foreign research agencies. As new shipments arrive at these stations, they are planted, and extensive notes are made on their growth characteristics. These notes are published or otherwise made available to any plant breeder who needs help in locating a specific characteristic that he wishes to incorporate in a new variety. The regional stations have the added responsibility of placing a portion of newly introduced germ plasm in storage at Fort Collins.

One of the first steps, therefore, in developing a new variety is to check the literature to see if any of the lots from the world collection of wheat, for example, have shown the desired characteristics. If so, the breeder begins making crosses between a good commercial variety and the lot or lots from the world collection that show most promise. If there are no such clues to guide him, the breeder must "screen" the world collection of wheats, consisting of approximately 20,000 different lots, until he finds one or more with the characters he wants. This may seem like a tremendous undertaking—and it is—but it would be far greater without easy access to the world collection, which has been accumulated over a period of nearly seventy-five years.

In the early years of plant introduction, many potentially valuable lots of seed were tested for one or two qualities, such as hardiness or yield, and discarded because they were not superior in these respects. Also, many old varieties of grains, fruits, and other crops once grown by farmers were replaced by new varieties, and the old ones have become extinct. Some of those might have great value now in developing new varieties to meet new demands. The world seed collections, and the modern facilities for taking care of them, should prevent such losses of potentially valuable germ plasm in the future. They will also serve as one of the great arsenals of modern science in the battle against hunger throughout the world.

Starving in the Midst of Plenty

Few discoveries of Department of Agriculture scientists have found wider application than those dealing with chemicals that regulate plant growth. Although there are many of these chemicals and there are hundreds of uses for them, the one that has had the greatest impact is 2,4-D, used as a selective weed killer on farms, golf courses, playgrounds, and lawns.

Percy W. Zimmermann, a plant physiologist who worked for the Boyce Thompson Institute for Plant Research, discovered that certain chemicals can alter the normal growth of plants and used some of these chemicals to induce stem cuttings to develop roots. His discovery stimulated other plant scientists, including John W. Mitchell of the Bureau of Plant Industry, and Ezra J. Kraus, head of the Department of Botany at the University of Chicago. During World War II, Kraus taught graduate students four days a week and spent the other three days at Beltsville, Maryland, with Mitchell, one of his former students, working on plant growth regulators.

In 1944, Paul C. Marth became Mitchell's assistant, and by that time 2,4-D was attracting attention as a growth regulator. Marth, L. P. Batjer, and Frank Gardner discovered that it and other compounds they were studying would prevent certain varieties of apples from dropping off the trees a few days before they were ready to harvest. Mitchell and Marth then discovered that 2,4-D would kill dandelions and other broadleaf weeds in lawns and pastures without damaging the grass. It kills broadleaf plants by speeding up their growth processes so much that the plants use up their food reserves and starve.

The experiments also provided an extra dividend. One day when Mitchell and Marth were spraying their grass plots, the wind blew the drift of their spray to a spot about fifteen feet away where poison ivy and Japanese honeysuckle were growing. The following day they noticed that leaves on both kinds of plants were yellow, and remembered the breeze of the previous day. This early observation led to further experiments that helped to establish the value of 2,4-D and related compounds as a practical control for many kinds of woody shrubs and vines. It is the most widely used of all the herbicides now available.

Curiosity with a Purpose

Curiosity, plus a desire to help tobacco growers of southern Maryland in 1918, led two scientists of the Bureau of Plant Industry to discover one of the basic laws of plant growth, a law which explains why some plants flower and develop seed only on the long days of summer, while others wait for the shorter days of autumn.

The men were Wightman W. Garner and Harry A. Allard of the Tobacco Division. They had wondered for years why the mammoth tobacco grown in Maryland kept on growing so long that it was killed by frost before it developed seed. The scientists had ruled out temperature, moisture, fertilization, and light intensity before they decided to test length of day.

Using three tobacco plants and a box of soybean seedlings, Garner and Allard gave them seventeen hours of darkness and only seven hours of daylight. They did this by moving the plants into a small darkened shack every afternoon at four o'clock. In a few days, the plants blossomed and began to form seed, convincing the scientists that a basic principle was involved. Trying several other kinds of plants, they found that plants differ in the proportions of day and night required for blooming and seed formation. This response of plants to light they called photoperiodism. Their discovery answered many questions but it raised many more, which were to challenge scientists for the next half-century. In fact, pieces of the puzzle are still being put together.

Garner and Allard spent the rest of their lives studying photoperiodism. They found that day length rather than temperature tells birds when it is time to migrate. Results of their work have been used by florists for years to make chrysanthemums and other potted plants bloom at any season by giving them the correct day length. Plant breeders used this knowledge to bring about simultaneous flowering of plants they wished to cross-pollinate.

In 1936, when the Bankhead-Jones Act made funds available for basic research, a special project was established on photoperiodism. Marion W. Parker and Harry A. Borthwick worked together for several years without achieving a breakthrough. In 1944, Borthwick was joined by Sterling B. Hendricks, an authority on plant nutrition. Together they made several important discoveries: (1) that plants use just one part of sunlight—the red—in launching growth changes; (2) that a hidden substance in plants triggers their growth changes; and (3) that this substance can exist in either of two forms, active and inactive, and that it can be changed from one to the other by exposure to the proper kind of light. At this point, one of their associates, Harold W. Siegelman, isolated the triggering substance in young corn plants.

The substance, named phytochrome by the scientists, controls growth from seed germination to flowering and fruiting. Since it can be made active or inactive, depending upon the wave length of light it receives, it is possible for man to make plants grow or stop growing, as desired. With such knowledge available to scientists, exciting possibilities lie ahead for tailoring plants to meet specific needs.

Protecting Our Plants and Animals

The damage done by Japanese beetles in recent years testifies to the need to protect plants and animals against foreign pests. Japanese beetles slipped into the United States in 1916, when quarantine enforcement was not as effective as it is now. In the half century since these insects arrived, they have ravaged countless orchards, flower and vegetable gardens, and lawns. The annual cost of controlling these and other introduced pests runs into the millions.

The size of the job can be imagined when we consider that 178 million people enter the United States every year. They bring more than 42 million pieces of baggage, each of which could be the hiding place of a new pest. Just one attractive orange has been found to contain hundreds of maggots of alien insects. One small piece of meat packed in a lunch box could be the means of bringing into the country a new livestock disease.

To protect the people of the United States against such risks, the Agricultural Research Service maintains a staff of inspectors at all airports, seaports, and border crossings. These men work closely with customs inspectors, frequently remaining in the background until called upon by customs men. These inspectors stop a potentially damaging pest every fifteen minutes around the clock.

Commercial shipments move through a system of permits, inspection, and treatment when it is necessary. The elaborate precautions taken with imported zoo animals has already been mentioned in Chapter II as one of the functions of the Animal Health Division. Advance inspection at point of origin by a recognized agency of government is a method also used with some plants. Because of the heavy shipment of bulbs to the United States, ARS inspectors now give prior clearance to bulbs from Holland, Belgium, France, Italy, and South Africa, working in cooperation with government officials in the country of origin. Shipments bearing a certificate of the cooperative inspection program go directly to U.S. purchasers.

Some of our worst pests slipped into the United States before we had quarantines to keep them out. When the Plant Quarantine Act became effective in 1912, we already had such well-known pests as hornflies, gypsy moths, San Jose scale, Argentine ants, boll weevils, and European corn borers. In the first fifteen years of the plant quarantine, the job was difficult enough, but it became doubly difficult with the advent of international air traffic.

Very few people deliberately try to smuggle prohibited plant or animal products into the country. Most of those who have such material in their possession have no idea that it can do harm—which only underlines the need for greater efforts to acquaint the traveling public with the facts. The ARS Information Division, working in cooperation with the Plant Quarantine Division, has produced notable results along these lines. (This work is used as an example of public relations in Chapter VI.)

In spite of all the planning and efforts to get public cooperation, quarantine activities make the headlines several times a year, and almost always the work is portrayed as a bother to travelers. High officials of the government are often the unintentional cause of some of the headlines. Prize stallions given to President Eisenhower and Mrs. John F. Kennedy caused some uneasy moments for ARS officials; the animals, however, were quarantined for the prescribed period, the same as other animals of less renown.

A most awkward situation arose when the Japanese Ambassador to the United States made a gift of more than 100 Japanese flowering cherry trees to the city of Washington to further the beautification program. The Secretary of the Interior promptly accepted the gift, which was made in the name of the Japanese people. Telephones rang and memos were dashed off to Interior, explaining that under the law Japanese cherry trees were specifically prohibited entry into the United States. There was good reason for the law, for the original gift of flowering cherries to the city of Washington early in the century, before passage of the plant quarantine law in 1912, had brought in several new diseases and insects. The trees were so badly infected that all of them died or were destroyed and were replaced with clean nursery stock. With this history to support them, ARS officials stood firm, and the Secretary of Agriculture backed them up.

Several weeks passed before a plan was worked out to allow the Japanese to purchase trees of the same varieties from American nurserymen. The solution to the problem did not receive as much attention in the newspapers as the earlier stories of wrangling between two members of the President's Cabinet.

At one time, the Agricultural Research Service was under pressure to allow importation of frozen meat from certain parts of Argentina that are said to be free of foot-and-mouth disease. Those in the agency who were closest to the problem firmly believed that importation of meat from Argentina in any form (except canned) would be taking an unnecessary risk for which our livestock industry might suffer. As of early 1967, the question had not yet been settled.

V

In the Service of Man

Water, water, everywhere—but will there be enough?

No one knows the answer to this question, but a large group of scientists in industry, universities, and government are hard at work, seeking an affirmative answer for the benefit of future generations. The Agricultural Research Service is vitally concerned, because water is necessary for food production, and agriculture is the biggest user of water in the United States. Any new concept or any new practice that results in more efficient use of water in agriculture is bound to benefit the rest of the country, for all of us are using water from the same source.

New Ways to Save Water

Hydrologists say that 97 per cent of the water on the surface of the earth is held in the oceans. Most of the other 3 per cent is locked up in the ice packs and glaciers of the Arctic and Antarctic regions. That leaves a small fraction of 1 per cent available for man, but man has not shown much concern for this natural resource. Only in the last half century has he made a concerted effort to do something about improving and conserving his tiny share of the earth's supply of water.

The story of ARS research on water comes into sharp focus against the background of the water situation in the United

States. We get our supply of water from precipitation, either as rain or snow. If all of the precipitation that falls on the continental United States were evenly distributed, all of our land would receive about thirty inches of water every year—a natural resource that places our country among the most favored in the entire world in this respect.

But 70 per cent of this precipitation is either used by plants or lost rather quickly by evapotranspiration, a word that hydrologists use to refer to the process in which water is transpired, or given off, by plants in the growing process and in which water is lost by evaporation from the soil surface. About half of the water used by plants is consumed by those that provide food and timber, but the other half is used by plants, such as mesquite, that have no economic value.

Here is a tremendous challenge to research. There are great opportunities to reduce the waste of water—for example, by finding practical ways to get rid of mesquite and other unwanted plants on the western ranges—and some progress has already been made in killing these plants with herbicides. Perhaps the greatest opportunity lies in management practices that make the most efficient use of water by crop plants.

Settlers in the Great Plains soon discovered that they could grow more wheat by planting every second year and keeping the land free of all vegetation on alternate years. This practice, known as fallowing, was an attempt to save up two years' supply of water for one crop. Research has brought about many refinements in fallowing and in crop rotation that make better use of available moisture in the plains. In regions of greater rainfall, terraces have been used for many years to reduce runoff following heavy rains. More recently, broad channel terraces have been developed to facilitate the use of the large machinery used on many farms.

In their search for ways to make better use of water, ARS scientists appear to be willing to try almost anything that looks promising, as the following examples show.

1. In the arid West, they are spraying impervious covers on hillsides and catching the runoff water for watering livestock. In some localities, they are replenishing ground water for irrigation by diverting runoff to storage in natural soil formations.

2. Experiments in North Dakota produced fifty bushels of corn per acre without irrigation with only four inches of rainfall during the growing season. The scientists ridged the area between the corn rows and covered the ridges with black plastic film. The rain drained off the plastic covering and was concentrated around the plants. Measurements showed that the corn plants received the equivalent of a two-and-a-half-inch rain from a quarter-inch shower.

3. An asphalt mixture that reduces seepage when sprayed on the soil surface or poured into ponds might be practical to reduce seepage in irrigation ditches and canals. In one experiment, this treatment cut seepage 80 per cent, at a cost of only 10 cents a square yard (compared with $1 a square yard for conventional materials used in lining canals and ditches).

4. A great variety of materials are being developed to control infiltration and runoff. A resin emulsion appears promising on sandy soils, decreases runoff, and controls wind and water erosion. It is also insoluble in water, durable, and yet porous enough for water to percolate into the soil and for seedlings to push their way up from the soil.

Scientists are finding ways for irrigation farmers to stretch their water supply through better timing of irrigations and more accurate knowledge of the water requirements of crops. In Texas, for example, ARS engineers demonstrated that grain sorghum can be produced with half the usual amount of irrigation water. This reduction not only saves water but also cuts the cost of the water itself and eases the inevitable problem of salinity, or "salty" soil.

When soils are irrigated for several years, they become saline, or salty. This is because irrigation water contains small quantities of salts. As moisture evaporates or is transpired by plants it passes into the atmosphere and the salts are left in the root zone of the soil unless they are flushed downward to ground water by rainfall or very heavy irrigation periodically. In the arid West, it is estimated that 25 per cent of all irrigated land has lost some value for crop production because of salinity, and millions of additional acres are in danger.

Much of man's early development was based on irrigation agriculture, and the ancient basin irrigation works of Egypt were the foundation for a rich culture for many centuries. It is interesting that 2,500 years before Christ, irrigation agriculture in Egypt was facing a situation strikingly similar to that in the United States today. The problems of salinity and its destructive effects on food production were recorded in documents that have come down to us from that time.

There is one big difference. For the last twenty-five years, the Department of Agriculture and the experiment stations of eighteen western states have been cooperating in a determined attack on salinity. The work is centered at the U.S. Salinity Laboratory of the Agricultural Research Service at Riverside, California. A wealth of useful information has come from this laboratory, but much more will be needed if irrigation agriculture is to continue as part of our way of life.

Mystery of Life

ARS scientists cover the waterfront. One group is trying to decide what to do about millions of acres of "salty" soils, while another group is probing a microscopic plant cell, searching an answer to one of the mysteries of life: How does a plant make protein? Not only are both groups in the Agricultural Research Service, they are both in the ARS Soil and Water Conservation Research Division.

A big step toward understanding how plant and animal cells manufacture protein was taken in 1965 by a team of biochemists, who determined the molecular structure of one of the RNA's (ribonucleic acids). This was the culmination of seven years of work for Robert W. Holley and his team of four ARS scientists and three scientists from Cornell University. Holley himself was with the Agricultural Research Service when the work began but transferred to Cornell about a year before the discovery was announced. It was a team effort, carried out at the U.S. Plant, Soil, and Nutrition Laboratory, on the campus at Cornell.

This was the first time that the structure of an RNA had been determined. The structurally identified RNA is a "transfer" RNA (abbreviated as tRNA). These are the smallest of the known biologically active nucleic acids. They select and carry activated amino acids to the protein-building sites within the cell. There the tRNA's align with each other along a template of other nucleic acids. The sequence of this alignment determines which protein will be synthesized. Protein synthesis, or building, is the process by which living cells convert food into new cell-building material. The kind of cells built determines what the organism will be—plant, animal, or human.

It is almost impossible to evaluate such a discovery, but this research may lead to ways of altering genetic characteristics of living organisms by modifying the structures of nucleic acids. The Department gave its highest honor, the Distinguished Service Award, to the group, and Dr. Holley received the Albert Lasker Basic Medical Research Award of $10,000.

A New Soil Science for America

When Curtis F. Marbut came to the Department of Agriculture from the University of Missouri in 1909, soil science in this country was influenced greatly by the views of Justus von Liebig, a renowned German scientist, who believed that the soil was a kind of reservoir from which man could take out only what he had supplied. The lack of wide variations in the soils of Western Europe and the need for constant applications of manures and fertilizers made Von Liebig's theory seem reasonable to scientists in Germany, France, and England.

The first chief of the Bureau of Soils, Milton Whitney, was sure that the theory did not apply to the soils of America. He went to the other extreme and said that all soils had sufficient nutrients to support plant growth and that yields of crops were determined by rainfall and other factors of climate, by mechanical condition of the soil and its management, and by the presence or absence of toxic compounds in the soil.

A school of eminent soil scientists had developed in Russia, where the large expanse of lands included wide differences in geographic features and soil characteristics. Some of the soils were extremely fertile, in contrast to the generally impoverished soils of Western Europe. The Russians went outdoors and studied their soils in fields and forests.

Curtis Marbut was placed in charge of the U.S. soil survey, which had already begun. He agreed with Whitney that the Von Liebig theory did not apply to our soils. He also recognized the contributions of the Russians and developed a program of field studies that included many of their ideas. He went further into the detailed study and classification of local soil types as a basis for making recommendations to individual farmers.

Marbut succeeded Whitney as the leading soil scientist in the country. He had the ability to see truth in each school of thought, and he used all of them to build a body of soil science that fitted conditions in the United States. He laid the foundation for the present system of soil classification and mapping. Although refinements in the system have been made since his death in 1935, he left the tools needed to build a modern soil science for the United States.

Penicillin: The Great Lifesaver

One of the great accomplishments of the Agricultural Research Service was the development of a method for making penicillin in commercial quantities during World War II. Dr. Alexander Fleming of England had discovered the unusual ability of penicillin to kill bacteria in 1928. Its value as an antibiotic had been demonstrated at Oxford University, but nothing had been done to produce penicillin in the large quantities needed to treat wounded servicemen. The British knew of the research on mold fermentations at the ARS Northern Utilization Laboratory in Peoria, Illinois. They brought a small sample of the mold that produces penicillin to Peoria in 1941 and asked for help. Taking advantage of the large collection of molds and the experience of its staff, the laboratory, with assistance from the University of Wisconsin and the Carnegie Institution of Washington, soon developed a method that was usable by industry for making large quantities of penicillin. Essentially, the research consisted of (1) finding the best microorganism from the millions available to produce penicillin, (2) finding the best food for the organism, and (3) perfecting a method to make the organism work in large vats used by industry as it had done on surface cultures at the laboratory.

Human Nutrition Research Begins

The concern of agricultural research for people, as well as animals, is illustrated by the fact that the first research in human nutrition in this country was done in the Department of Agriculture. Dr. Wilbur O. Atwater, head of the Chemistry Department at Wesleyan University, Middletown, Connecticut, and director of the first agricultural experiment station in the nation, became interested in human nutrition as a graduate student at Yale and went to Germany for further study. When he returned, he and two associates at Wesleyan built a respiration calorimeter (metabolism chamber), in which to study the energy relations of nutrition to the human body.

Atwater served as the first chief of the Office of the Experiment Stations from 1888 until 1891, and when Congress appropriated funds to the Department of Agriculture for human nutrition studies in 1894, he was appointed special agent in charge, with headquarters at Wesleyan University. Several state stations cooperated, but the major work was done by Atwater and his assistants, who conducted over 500 experiments in their metabolism chamber. Students of the university often served as experimental subjects, eating and sleeping in the chamber, pedaling a stationary bicycle, and doing other "guinea pig" chores along with their regular schoolwork.

Studies of diets of persons in different occupations in this country were compared with those of persons in other countries. The scientists made many experiments on human digestion and special studies on the nutritive values of many common foods and the effects of cooking or other preparation on these nutritive values. Using the results of the many dietary studies and analyses of foods, Atwater compiled the nation's first extensive table of food values, which was published in 1896 as Office of Experiment Stations Bulletin 28.

Atwater was trying to discover the best and most economical diet for man. At that time only protein and calories supplied by fats and carbohydrates were considered important; green, leafy vegetables and fruits were regarded as luxuries. His interest in nutrition encompassed the entire population. He wanted to learn how the national food production could be made to yield the best returns in economic progress and social welfare.

Atwater and his associates firmly established human nutrition as a major branch of science. Because it was so closely related to food production, it was natural that this new science should be associated with the state experiment stations and the Department of Agriculture.

Are We Eating Too Much?

Because of nutrition research and the wide dissemination of its results through magazines, newspapers, other publications, radio, and television, Americans are paying more attention to what they eat than ever before. Many are counting calories, watching their weights, and remembering the green and yellow vegetables. We have more information on good nutrition than any people have ever had, and it's all free for the asking. Any homemaker today who has adequate funds and who can read has no excuse for serving her family meals that add up to poor diets.

One of the absorbing topics under investigation in the Human Nutrition Research Division is the effect of diets on length of life. Results tend to confirm the popular belief that diet does affect the life-span, but no sweeping generalizations can be made. Even when nutritionally adequate diets were fed to laboratory animals, different diets resulted in differences in survival. The scientists think these differences are due, in part at least, to the way an animal makes use of various combinations of food.

The combination of foods seemed to have more influence on the way the body responded than the individual foods being tested. Rats lived as long on a 100 per cent egg diet as on a synthetic diet with no egg. However, when they were fed a diet of 25 per cent egg together with certain carbohydrates, the life-span was shortened significantly. Another indication of the interaction of foods comes from studies of different combinations of particular fats and carbohydrates in the diet. In experimental animals, a high incidence of kidney stones occurred when a particular diet contained lactose and butter oil. The stones were rarely seen when the diet contained lactose and corn oil, and they were completely absent when cornstarch replaced lactose as the carbohydrate, regardless of whether the fat was butter oil or corn oil.

The research shows that heredity plays a large part in the reactions of animals to diet. When two strains of rats were fed a diet containing sugar and 25 per cent egg, there was an average difference of 200 days—about one-third of the normal life expectancy of rats—between the two strains. Overeating seems to be as bad for rats as it is for men. Experiments show that rats that ate excessive amounts and gained weight at a rapid rate died at an earlier age, regardless of the composition of the diet.

Another part of the food research story of the Agricultural

Research Service deals with food plans that help homemakers balance meals and budgets. These plans are based upon research in the Service and elsewhere, and are made available free to homemakers who request them from county extension agents or from the Department of Agriculture. The plans are contained in a series of publications, which begins with *Food for the Young Couple* and concludes with *Food Guide for Older Folks*.

New Hope for Protein-Hungry Peoples

Sometimes a simple experiment can have profound implications. This truth is illustrated by feeding tests at the Purdue University Agricultural Experiment Station showing that an unusual type of corn, when fed alone, produced as good gains with pigs as ordinary corn supplemented with soybean meal to provide the kind of protein that animals require (but which corn lacks). This discovery suggests the possibility of saving millions of dollars for pork producers and consumers, but the most exciting implications in this research relate to the feeding of people rather than pigs.

Corn is one of the most widely grown crops in the world and is an important source of human food in Central and South America and in central Africa, two of the large areas of the world that are deficient in protein. It can also be grown in other areas of the world where diets are low in protein.

The protein in corn, as well as that in other cereals used as human food, is lacking in two of the amino acids (the building blocks from which protein is made) required by animals, including man. For this reason American farmers add a protein supplement such as soybean meal to corn fed to livestock.

Animal proteins such as eggs, meat, and milk contain all of the essential amino acids for man, but these foods are scarce in most of the developing countries. Beans help to provide the necessary amino acids in diets of people in Central and South America, and other foods are used in other areas. However, the lack of protein, both in quality and quantity, is a major problem of human nutrition in many parts of the world.

This is why agricultural scientists are excited about the feeding experiments at Purdue. If the genetic characters (genes) in the special kind of corn fed to the pigs at Purdue can be successfully transferred to commercial hybrid corn with its better balance of amino acids, this crop will be vastly improved as feed for livestock and as food for humans. American farmers will not have to buy as much soybean meal for their pigs, and millions of the world's peoples will no longer be subject to nutritional diseases that bring death to small children and impair the health of adults.

The outlook for such developments is promising. Corn breeders are already using the genes for high-quality protein in developing new hybrids, and there is a good possibility that these improved hybrids (with more of the essential amino acids) will be available for farmers to plant by 1970.

An intensive search is in progress to locate genes that can similarly improve the quality of the protein in wheat, rice, and other grains. The task will be a big one, as thousands of varieties, strains, and unnamed individual selections (plants) must be analyzed for amino acid content. Scientists make no predictions as to the outcome, but they are hopeful of success.

Making Milk Safe to Drink

In the early 1900's, milk was often produced and sold under conditions that resulted in contamination with many spoilage organisms and, in some cases, germs of tuberculosis, undulant fever, or other serious diseases. Some of these organisms multiplied rapidly and caused the milk to sour within a few days. This was considered by many to be nature's way of keeping milk off the dinner table when it was no longer safe to drink.

A group of young bacteriologists in the Dairy Division challenged that idea. One of them was Samuel Henry Ayers, who was convinced that the only way to produce completely safe milk was to pasteurize it. The practice was first recommended as a health measure in 1875, but some people in positions of responsibility believed that it would do more harm than good. They argued that pasteurization destroyed the lactic acid bacteria in milk, causing it to decompose instead of souring. It was also thought that destruction of the lactic acid bacteria allowed the growth of toxin-producing organisms that made pasteurized milk unfit for human consumption.

Ayers made a painstaking study of milk, recording the presence of bacteria in raw and pasteurized milk obtained from retail outlets of several cities. He made thousands of counts of bacteria. His work, first published in 1910, showed that pasteurization did not destroy all of the lactic acid forming bacteria, that organisms did not multiply faster in milk that had been pasteurized, and that pasteurization merely prolonged the condition of clean raw milk. His publications convinced many physicians and public officials that pasteurized milk was safer than raw milk. These publications take their place beside the most illustrious ever issued by the Department of Agriculture.

New Kinks for Cotton

An exciting race is being run to see who can produce the finest, fanciest, and thriftiest fabrics for housewives who don't like the chore of ironing. The contestants are scientists from the Agricultural Research Service and the textile industry who are trying to improve cotton and wool, and the equally resourceful scientists in industry who are creating new synthetics and improving the old ones. The race can be properly described as an endurance contest, which is likely to continue for many years. The stakes are high, and the winners will not be the chemists but American consumers.

Several early heats of the race were won by the synthetics group. One of the first victories was rayon strong enough to use for tire cords. Tire manufacturers quickly switched from cotton to rayon because of price, and growers lost a market for more than a million bales of cotton each year. Another big blow for growers was the success of men's shirts made of synthetic fiber that needed little ironing. In the meantime, nylon was threatening to take over the market for women's garments and for many household uses that cotton had always filled.

The chemists and engineers at the Southern Utilization Research Laboratory and their counterparts in industry then threatened to close the gap. They made a series of basic discoveries on ways to make cotton behave like the synthetics, when washed and hung up to dry, and still retain the desirable properties of cotton. Various resins were developed that would make cotton drip-dry. Some of the large shirtmakers gave a boost to the cotton team by increasing their research on cotton, when they discovered that many men found that shirts made from synthetics were not as comfortable as those made from cotton. From this effort in the 1950's came the first wash-wear cotton shirts, which needed only a little ironing. Next came shirts, trousers, and other articles made by a new process from a blend of 35 per cent cotton with 65 per cent synthetics, which, after washing and either tumble- or drip-drying, needed no ironing at all and had permanent creases.

But scientists at New Orleans and their colleagues in industry were not willing to settle for 35 or even 50 per cent cotton in men's shirts, underwear, pajamas, and sports clothes. They wanted the entire market for cotton. A point in their favor was that garments made from the blend were not as durable as those made from all cotton. They won the next race, and since 1965 consumers have been able to buy all-cotton shirts that are durable and look newly pressed after repeated launderings and dryings. The durability problem for garments made from heavier-weight fabrics, such as men's and boys' trousers, had not been fully overcome, but the goal was in sight, and the growers were expected to regain a large part of this market, which involves millions of bales of cotton.

Secret of the new process is a treatment for the fabric that takes effect only after the garment is made, pressed, and set with heat. The fabric is thus set in the shape of the garment and returns to this shape after laundering and drying.

The race, however, is not confined to fabrics designed to separate the housewife from the ironing board. Stretch fabrics zoomed in popularity several years ago; again the synthetics jumped off to a big lead. Now cotton is making a comeback, and 60 million yards of fabrics are treated each year to make them stretch. The process is known as slack mercerization. It was discovered 125 years ago, when John Mercer, an English chemist, noted that when caustic soda was poured through cotton filter cloth, it caused the threads to contract. A century later, a chemist at the Southern Utilization Research Laboratory used this information to make cotton stretch bandages that are much more comfortable and less expensive than those made of elastic. After stretch garments made of synthetics became popular, other scientists used Mercer's discovery to make the stretch cotton that is now used in a wide variety of garments.

Permanent Creases for Wool

When Albert Edward, Prince of Wales, introduced the style of wearing trousers creased down the front, he created a problem for men that lasted almost three-quarters of a century. A process for putting permanent creases in wool developed at the ARS Western Utilization Research Laboratory may solve the problem and help keep wool competitive with man-made fibers.

The Prince of Wales (later Edward VII) began wearing trousers with center creases in the late years of the nineteenth century. There is a legend that he tried on a pair of trousers at his tailor's that had been folded and laid aside in such a way that creases had formed down the front and back. They made him look slender, so he began wearing trousers creased that way. In a short time, the new fashion created in London had spread to most of the Western world.

Like cotton, wool is also getting a going-over from research. It too was losing markets to synthetics designed for modern living, but research at the Western Utilization Research Laboratory has made wool modern enough for any need. Besides treating wool to give it a permanent crease, scientists have made it shrinkproof. Almost every housewife has learned to her sorrow not to put ordinary woolen garments in a washing machine. Sox that go in size 12 may come out size 7 or 8. But wool is different now. Several manufacturers are making shrink-proof wool apparel that can be machine-washed and tumble-dried. Others are making suits that stretch, and the U.S. Quartermaster Corps has approved wool uniforms with permanent creases for the armed forces. Additional research is aiming for wool that is moth-proof, stretchable, crease retaining, soil resisting, and longer wearing.

The race continues, with synthetic fiber chemists bringing out new and better fibers made from petroleum, while scientists working with cotton and wool add more and more desirable properties to these natural fibers.

Plastic Foams From Castor Oil

An economical process developed by the Agricultural Research Service for altering the properties of castor oil extends the potential usefulness of this farm product in the manufacture of lightweight plastics known as urethane foams. Foams made from castor oil have more resistance to water and shrinkage than similar foams made from petrochemicals, which are being used increasingly for upholstering materials, thermal and acoustical insulation, crash pads, lightweight structural materials, and other specialty products.

ARS officials believe that the building industry provides a very large potential market for plastic foams made from castor oil. A unique feature of the new foams is that they can be produced on the spot where they are to be used. A reactive liquid mixture is poured into empty spaces in walls, floors, or roofs, where it immediately foams up and fills the space with a rigid foam that gives strength and provides a stable barrier against heat, sound, and vapors. The castor oil foams can also be made flame resistant without losing their other properties and at significantly lower cost than similar fire-resistant foams made from petrochemicals. Several industrial firms have become interested in the new foams, which could result in large increases in castor bean acreage in the United States.

Crambe: A Promising New Crop for Industrial Use

In 1960, few people in the United States had heard of crambe, a member of the mustard family of plants. Plant explorers had introduced it a few years before as a possible source of oil to replace imported rapeseed oil in industry. By 1966, crambe was showing unusual promise as a new oilseed crop that would not compete with those grown in the United States. It is adapted to many areas of the West and Middle West where wheat is grown.

In studies at the Northern Utilization Research Laboratory and in tests by the steel industry, crambe oil has proved superior to lubricants used in the continuous casting of steel to keep the hot metal from sticking to the molds and cracking them. The oil also shows promise as a source of chemicals for use in manufacturing nylon, plastics, and waxes.

When the oil has been extracted from the seed, the residue is a high-protein meal; parallel studies have been aimed at developing a use for the meal. Like almost all oilseeds, crambe contains substances that would lower the feeding value of the meal if they were not inactivated or removed by processing. Scientists at the Northern Laboratory found that treating crambe meal with ammonia inactivates unpalatable and harmful compounds. The process is practical and can be adapted to existing oilseed plants. Feeding tests confirm reports from the laboratory that all harmful substances are removed by the ammonia treatment.

The Pacific Vegetable Oil Corporation, Richmond, California, contracted with farmers to grow and harvest about 1,000 acres of crambe in 1965. The firm processed the seed to obtain oil and meal, and marketed these products. Scientists at the Northern Utilization Research Laboratory served as advisers to the corporation in adapting the latest research results to the processing of crambe.

Insecticides by the Drop

One of the most significant new developments in the use of insecticides is the method worked out by the Agricultural Research Service of applying an insecticide (malathion) as an undiluted spray, instead of diluting it with a large amount of water or oil. By making necessary adjustments in spray nozzles and other equipment, it is now possible to distribute a few ounces evenly over an entire acre of land. By the late 1950's, there was considerable agitation to reduce the amount of pesticides used by farmers and government agencies in an effort to eliminate unnecessary residues. Scientists, moreover, have always sought to use the smallest effective amount of pesticides in an effort to keep down the costs.

A Methods Improvement Group was created in the Plant Pest Control Division, at Gulfport, Mississippi, to test ideas that promised to improve plant pest control programs, and the new method was developed there. Malathion was chosen because it is one of the insecticides least toxic to warm-blooded animals, and the residue lasts only a few days after application.

The new method, known as low-volume malathion, was first tested against grasshoppers in 1962. Results were so good that it became the standard treatment in the next grasshopper control program, in 1964. With this method only 8 ounces of malathion per acre were needed, about half the quantity previously used. In reporting results, the entomologists said that only minor adjustments in the spray equipment were required; the biggest adjustment was in adjusting to the idea of covering an acre effectively with only a half-pint of liquid.

Savings with low-volume spraying have been dramatic. Time

for loading and ferrying airplanes to the control area in the grasshopper program was cut by almost 90 per cent. In the boll weevil control program in Texas a year later, one flight covered as much land as twenty-seven flights had done under the old method. One reason for this is the fact that malathion is non-volatile, and can be dispersed at higher altitudes, making it possible to cover a swath 100 feet wide instead of 35 feet wide as in the past. In control operations against the cereal leaf beetle in Michigan, dosage was cut from 16 ounces of malathion per acre to 5.3 ounces. Total cost of material and application was reduced by 65 per cent, and the treatment was more effective.

Following the successful use of low-volume applications from airplanes, ARS agricultural engineers teamed up with entomologists to build a ground sprayer for control of sweet corn pests in cooperation with the Georgia Coastal Plains Experiment Station at Tifton. Parts for the four-row machine cost $300. Other ground equipment has been developed in cooperative research at State College, Mississippi, and at Florence, South Carolina. All such equipment has been reported successful.

Aerosol for All

If the two scientists of the Agricultural Research Service who developed aerosal containers for dispersing insecticides in 1942 had been told at that time how universally their invention would be used twenty-five years later, they would not have believed it. No product of agricultural research has ever found more uses by people than the aerosol container. It is another illustration of the fact that all knowledge is potentially useful to man.

Lyle D. Goodhue, a chemist, and William N. Sullivan, an entomologist, were looking for more efficient ways to disperse insecticides in enclosed areas when they made the first aerosol by spraying pyrethrum on a hot surface to produce a fog of extremely small droplets. They improved their original idea by dissolving an insecticide in a liquefied gas under pressure in a container. When this was released, the liquid became a vapor that carried the particles of insecticide to all parts of an enclosed space, killing all insects present.

The discovery came just in time to be used by troops in World War II. The original containers resembled hand grenades, and were called aerosol bombs. More than 40 million were manufactured for the armed forces, and they became standard equipment for all troops in tropical areas. Later models used the lightweight cans that have become so popular for dispensing dozens of items in everyday use in millions of homes throughout the world.

VI

ARS and the Public

In mathematics, the whole is equal to the sum of all its parts. This law does not hold true for institutions, and the Agricultural Research Service is a good example. Because of its large size and the wide diversity of its activities, some parts of ARS loom larger in the public mind than the agency itself.

One of these is the National Arboretum, a popular attraction to the thousands of visitors who come to Washington in the spring, as well as to the residents of the Washington, D.C., area. Its identification as part of the Agricultural Research Service is of no particular concern to those who view the dazzling display of 100,000 azaleas blooming on a hillside under towering oak trees. A Secretary of Agriculture who had been in office only a short while was driven to the aboretum to see the azaleas. Visibly impressed by the beauty all around him, he asked who was in charge of this delightful place. His chauffeur replied, "You are, boss."

Many of the developments of ARS scientists are well known, but their origin is not. Most people who use frozen orange juice, instant mashed potatoes, drip-dry cottons, and the new machine-washable woolens do not associate these with ARS or even with the Department of Agriculture. At one time, it was considered bad taste for a research agency to call attention to itself or its accomplishments. The Agricultural Research Service evolved from such a tradition, and although it is striving to become better known, it is doing so in the manner expected of a well-established public research agency.

The great majority of people in this country do not know of the existence of ARS. Newspapers in the large cities occasionally run a front-page story on some unusual aspect of its activities—such as whether a cargo of zoo animals will be allowed to unload at New York after making a stop in a country known to have dangerous livestock diseases. Even then, the name of Department of Agriculture is much more likely to appear in the story than that of the Agricultural Research Service. In urban centers, those who have received popular publications on foods, homemaking, or gardening may be aware of ARS as the scientific arm of the Department of Agriculture.

Where ARS Is Known

The agricultural public is much more knowledgeable about ARS, as might be expected. At any given time, several thousand farmers and ranchers may be cooperating with the agency in disease eradication campaigns and will have considerable knowledge of what it does. People who read farm magazines or listen to farm broadcasts learn about results of ARS work. However, in reporting work done in cooperation with the states, the magazine or broadcasting station usually prefers to credit the state agency on the assumption that it will be better known and therefore more likely to be accepted as authoritative.

Professional and business groups in agriculture are generally well informed about ARS and hold it in high regard. Research workers in states, industry, and private foundations, usually keep abreast of the results of ARS research related to their own fields. Many workers at the state stations have offices in the same buildings as federal workers and may even be cooperating with the man next door. Proximity also occurs in regulatory activities. State and industry officials are quite familiar with ARS and are generally strong supporters. Regulatory work is well coordinated with the states.

ARS also has excellent relations with farm and commodity organizations, which may often be critical of the farm program activities of the Department of Agriculture but not of ARS research. An organization of cotton growers and processors has been one of the most consistent supporters of ARS research and its most effective lobbyist for increased funds. Other groups lobby for other commodities. A group representing flour millers, transportation, and the grain trade has been very effective in getting congressional support for research on grains, and for strengthening the protection of our agriculture against foreign pests.

The scientific public is not as aware of ARS as might be expected, although there are some notable exceptions. Biological scientists, for example, learn a great deal about the agency from their journals. The Service is a heavy contributor to many professional society journals in the life sciences, agricultural engineering, and soil science. The same is true of journals in chemistry, especially in the field of biochemistry.

In other branches of science there is less awareness of ARS. This may be based in part upon a lack of understanding of the character of ARS research. Fifty years ago, the scientific bureaus in the Department of Agriculture were concerned mainly with problem-solving research, and most of the problems concerned farming. Hence, the Department was tagged by scientists as a research agency for farmers. The last two chapters have shown how far the Agricultural Research Service has moved in the last half century into broad and basic studies that affect all sciences and all people. The Service has not moved away from the problems of agriculture; it has tried to keep abreast of them, and that requires exploration on many frontiers. Not many research agencies, however, can compete with the National Aeronautics and Space Administration or the National Institutes of Health for space in newspapers and magazines and for radio and TV time.

That fact must be understood in appraising public relations of the Agricultural Research Service.

The fact that the agency is not as well known as it might be raises two interesting questions: What does the agency think of this? And what is being done to make its work known to more people?

Part of the answer to the first question is that there are many scientists in ARS who are not at all concerned with its public image. They want the tools to work with, and they want to be left alone so they can get on with their jobs. They feel that a scientific institution should not be greatly concerned with public relations and point to other respected research agencies in the government that are no better known to the general public. They want their work known to other scientists, but feel that this is being done satisfactorily through scientific publications. They look with some suspicion on scientists whose work is written up frequently in newspapers and popular magazines.

This is not the view of ARS officials. They agree that it would be improper for the organization to forsake its scientific heritage and make bold claims for recognition, but there is still much room, they insist, to make the services of their agency known to many who, as consumers, especially in urban areas, need these services and could benefit from them.

This opinion is shared by friends of ARS outside the federal government. Among the most vocal of these groups are the research advisory committees. These committees have urged the Agricultural Research Service to make greater efforts to reach a larger public, and some of their suggestions have been adopted. Some commodity organizations have also recommended greater efforts to seek recognition. Agency heads operate under the close scrutiny of Congress, which enacted legislation many years ago forbidding executive branches of the government to employ "press agents." The law has never been repealed, and each department is required to submit every two years a list of all persons engaged in preparing and distributing information to the press. With this implied warning from Congress ringing in his ears, but with the friends of ARS urging him on, the Administrator of the Agricultural Research Service must be careful but courageous in his public relations.

It is a safe assumption, however, that ARS would like to be known more widely. This leads to the next question: What is being done to bring this about?

To appraise recent developments in ARS public relations, it is necessary to know what it has been doing all along in this area. All employees influence public attitudes toward a government agency, but those who play the greatest role are the top officials and those directly engaged in disseminating information. Since its creation in 1953, ARS has sought to cultivate good public relations. Top officials have understood that their decisions and actions may have more to do with public relations than any of the services conducted by the Information Division to keep the public informed of ARS activities. In the main, these officials have kept this fact in mind in their daily operations.

ARS and the Mass Media

The principal means of maintaining good public relations on a day-to-day basis in ARS has always been the reporting of its work to the public, and it is not likely to change this basic policy. Reporting to the public is planned around the three audiences referred to earlier in this chapter: the general public, the agricultural public, and the scientific public.

The general public learns about the work of ARS through newspapers, magazines, radio and television, and the many publications prepared especially for homemakers, homeowners, and gardeners. Of the ten most widely distributed publications of USDA in fiscal year 1966, eight dealt with ARS subject matter: *Family Fare* (a book of recipes tested by state and federal nutritionists), *Removing Stains from Fabrics, Food for Fitness* (a brief and simple daily food guide), *Family Food Stockpile for Survival, Defense Against Radioactive Fallout on the Farm,*

Roses for the Home, Consumers' Guide to USDA Services (a list of services available from ARS and the Consumers and Marketing Service), and *Vegetables in Family Meals.* It is significant that only one of these publications deals with farming.

Total distribution of these eight publications during fiscal year 1966 exceeded 2.5 million copies. It would seem that such large numbers of publications, year after year from one agency, would eventually make that agency well known to many readers. No precise information is available on this point, but it is quite likely that most people who receive these publications think of them as coming from the Department of Agriculture rather than from the Agricultural Research Service. This is because of the centralized publication distribution system and the policy that plays up the name of the Department on publications, rather than the names of the agencies. This policy also applies in all information work of the Department and accounts for the fact that the U.S. Department of Agriculture is better known than any of its agencies, with the possible exception of the Forest Service.

The agricultural public is served in numerous ways. Special efforts are made to keep agricultural leaders informed—leaders in research, extension, education, and industry. Extension workers in the states and counties, in frequent touch with farmers and homemakers, provide the best outlet for research information. They look to ARS to supplement the information provided by their own state experiment stations. The agricultural public includes approximately 12,000 teachers of agriculture and home economics in high schools throughout the country. These teachers use research information in their classrooms and as source material for special assignments.

Agricultural leaders are served by the ARS monthly magazine, *Agricultural Research,* by free copies of all popular ARS publications, and by special reports on research and regulatory work.

Farmers, who make up a large part of the agricultural public, are served directly through free distribution of Farmers Bulletins and other popular publications, and indirectly through reports prepared for the mass media—press, radio, TV, motion pictures, and exhibits. The first popular publication of the Department of Agriculture was issued by the Office of Experiment Stations in 1889; it was called a Farmers Bulletin, and the name was adopted for all popular publications dealing with subjects of interest to farmers. For many years, this series included most of the Department's popular publications, but in 1950 a new series, Home and Garden Bulletins, was established in recognition of the fact that the majority of Farmers Bulletins were actually of interest to homemakers, homeowners, and gardeners. This is now the Department's most popular series by far. Popular publications are distributed by the Federal Extension Service, by members of Congress, and by the Department in response to direct requests. Approximately 13 million copies a year are distributed; more than three-fourths of these publications are prepared by the Agricultural Research Service.

Mass media—the farm press, radio, and TV in particular—have always played a large part in supplying information to farmers. There are more than 300 farm magazines in the country, and they rely upon ARS as a dependable source of information. The larger ones use Department of Agriculture news releases primarily to keep abreast of progress. Their own staff members visit ARS laboratories and field stations to learn of the latest research. But most of these publications lack newsgathering staffs and are more likely to use news releases as issued, with only slight rewriting to adapt them to local interests. A recent trend in farm magazines has been highly specialized publications covering only one field. Examples are *Dairy Herd Management*, for dairymen, *Feed Lot*, for farmers who buy pigs or young steers and "finish" them for market by a period of heavy feeding, *Turkey World*, for turkey growers, and *Irrigation Age*, for irrigation farmers. Such publications are often part of a chain, with centralized circulation, advertising, and business operations. Most of them regularly use information originating in the Agricultural Research Service.

The development of radio and television has provided farmers with another good source of information. In the early days of radio, the Department of Agriculture and the state agricultural colleges could get as much time as they could use on farm programs; the National Farm and Home Hour, for example, was on the air for one hour, five days a week, for several years. The short time now allotted to farm programs on radio allows for little more than mention of new research, with a word on how to obtain additional details—usually in a publication. ARS has met the challenge of reduced radio time with brief, lively tapes that are tailored for one-, two-, or three-minute segments in the shortest farm programs. These tapes are sent free by the Department's Office of Information to all radio stations requesting this service.

It is about as easy for an agency such as the Agricultural Research Service to get time on television as on radio, if video tapes are supplied. Broadcasting stations are under obligation to the Federal Communications Commission to give a minimum of time to public service broadcasts, and program directors are glad to get well-prepared tapes or short films from public agencies. In recent years, the Service has established a good reputation with its series of "Beltsville newsreels," which run from two to ten or twelve minutes and picture research of interest to the general public, conducted at Beltsville or elsewhere. These films are used by more than 100 TV stations, and are passed from station to station until they have completed the circuit. When a news event, such as the 1959 visit of Nikita Khrushchev to Beltsville is involved, film prints are made immediately and sent to all the stations at once.

Video tapes have been used to especially good advantage in some ARS regulatory work. In the brucellosis eradication campaign, for example, the task of winning approval of farmers and ranchers was helped considerably by the use of video tapes explaining the need for cooperation.

The Agricultural Research Service serves the scientific public primarily through articles prepared by the scientists for publication in professional society journals. These articles report original research, and are considered by most scientists as the preferred method of keeping colleagues informed of their work. Most professional societies have no income except membership dues, and the rising cost of printing has forced many societies to increase dues and charge members additional fees for printing their articles. In effect, this system required that scientists become their own publishers, and many could not afford it. Most of the journals now have a schedule of page costs, which research institutions are expected to pay. ARS was among the first federal agencies to assume this cost and relieve its employees of an unfair burden.

Another means of reaching the scientific public is through technical publications of the Department of Agriculture—monographs, technical bulletins, research reports, and statistical bulletins. These publications are usually much longer and cover more phases of an investigation than is possible in the shorter articles required for professional journals. ARS averages about fifty technical publications a year. They are available at all college and university libraries and at many large public libraries. Many can be purchased at nominal prices from the Superintendent of Documents, Government Printing Office, Washington, D.C. The National Agricultural Library of the Department of Agriculture has an excellent photoreproduction service covering all technical agricultural publications.

From this brief résumé of its information program, it is apparent that the Agricultural Research Service knows its audience and has developed effective methods of reaching all of it except the general public. The measure of an information program, however, is not based entirely upon coverage. Equally important is the philosophy that determines policies and guides daily activities. Considering its conservative tradition as an old-line scientific agency, ARS follows a fairly liberal information policy, operating on the assumption that it has a duty to report results of research as widely as possible. It is true that it often has sought detailed accuracy at the expense of clarity in news releases on research, and some of its scientists do not like to have popular accounts of their work appearing simultaneously with technical accounts in professional journals. ARS scientists have about as much freedom to publish as anyone could wish. The agency allows them to choose the journals for their articles and shares the cost of publication. The only requirement is that a copy of each article be sent to the Information Division, as a guide to its writers in selecting subjects for news releases on research. These popular items are never released before journal publication and often appear in *Agricultural Research* two or three months later. Authors of scientific articles and their supervisors review all news releases.

In general, the system works very well; the division directors and others who review information materials are sympathetic to the need for simple, clear, and accurate reporting. Most reporters who are familiar with ARS feel that it operates a sound information service that they can trust. They also appreciate the fact that they have access to ARS officials and employees at any level, at any time.

Public Relations

The same general policy operates in the regulatory part of ARS. Regulatory work calls for action—sometimes preventive, sometimes remedial. Action programs always require educational efforts to inform those who will be affected. In research, it may be argued that a scientist should refrain from talking about his work publicly until he has completed it and can announce results. No such practice can be tolerated in a regulatory agency, which must be willing to discuss its work at every opportunity, explaining the why as well as the what, when, and where. In some cases, the success of an ARS regulatory program has been determined by the kind of information work carried on in advance of and in conjunction with the program itself.

Regulatory officials are subjected to far more criticism from

Congress, the press, and the public than research officials, and there is often a temptation to try to move in and do the job first and then announce its completion. This procedure nearly always backfires, because those who are affected lack the understanding and sympathetic attitude required for cooperation. At such times, the best information efforts are bound to be too little and too late. The Agricultural Research Service is trying to avoid such mistakes.

For example, in the campaign to eradicate the Mediterranean fruit fly in Florida in 1956, a senior member of the Information Division was sent to Florida to handle public information and advise on public relations. This experience led to formation of a small group in the Information Division to assist the regulatory divisions. Now every major campaign includes an information man assigned on a full-time basis. Because of this group, information workers now have more opportunity to make suggestions, especially in the planning stages of a campaign. This is still a relatively new idea, and could be developed further with benefit to the agency and its programs.

Another example of the growing awareness in ARS of the value of good public relations is its aggressive efforts to keep consumers informed of its activities. It is now standard practice to emphasize consumer interests in current progress reports of all kinds. Special efforts are made to supply useful information to magazines and editors of women's pages in newspapers. ARS-prepared radio and television material emphasizes consumer interests more than ever before. The same is true of ARS popular publications, which include more titles of interest to consumers than to farmers. The agency also gives strong support to all Department of Agriculture special events that provide an opportunity to inform writers and broadcasters of its own services to consumers.

The ARS has been actively participating in the national beautification program. Plant explorers are especially active in introducing plants that can be used to beautify homes, parks, streets, and highways. Special trips have been made in search of such plants, and several have been brought back for trial. The beautiful new headquarters building at the National Aboretum in Washington provides facilities for many meetings and events that call attention to the agency as a source of information on ornamental plants.

There are several hundred ARS field locations (a list will be found in Appendix C), and each is open to the public every working day. Special days are planned, when the public is invited to observe results of the work of these stations. For many years an organized effort has been made to welcome visitors to the Agricultural Research Center at Beltsville, Maryland, and to show them the work going on there. In 1967 this responsibility was assigned to the Information Division.

One of the best examples of how improved public relations can help to attain agency objectives is shown in enforcement of plant quarantines. As we have seen, the steady increase in foreign travel has magnified the danger of introducing new diseases and insects into the United States. Customs inspectors cooperate fully, but the threat continues to grow.

In 1963, an information specialist was assigned to organize an educational campaign. It was generally conceded that most travelers who attempt to bring in fruits or other items harboring foreign pests do so in ignorance of the danger to U.S. agriculture, so the first job was to inform all passengers on airlines and steamships. The problem of keeping pests out of the country was explained to airline and steamship officials and they were asked to cooperate. The first campaign materials were brochures and exhibits, explaining that certain items could not be brought into the U.S. A short motion picture was made and offered for showing on shipboard, and special exhibits were prepared for foreign airports. Written statements were prepared in several languages.

Americans returning home from abroad have consistently required close attention. To reach this group, the Passport

Office of the State Department agreed to include a statement on plant quarantines with the material given to U.S. citizens who apply for passports. U.S. State Department officials in Europe, South America, and Japan were provided with leaflets for distribution to prospective visitors to America. Meetings were also held with officials of the Military Aircraft Transport Service to enlist their cooperation. Warnings about quarantines are now included in military travel orders.

These activities have not yet stopped travelers from attempting to bring prohibited items into the country. At the end of 1966, however, the campaign was making good progress, and since the campaign began, there has been a decrease of 25 per cent in the number of prohibited items intercepted for each 1,000 pieces of baggage inspected.

VII

ARS and Other Agencies

Active cooperation with other agencies has always been a characteristic of ARS and its parent bureaus—especially cooperation with the state agricultural experiment stations and the state departments of agriculture. In more recent years, there has been increased cooperation with other agencies in the U.S. Department of Agriculture, with other departments of the federal government, with research institutions in foreign countries, and with industry.

State Experiment Stations

Cooperation between the Department of Agriculture and the state experiment stations is unique in the history of agricultural research. From its beginning, it has been a true partnership, based upon the common goal of making agriculture more productive. The tremendous advances in U.S. agriculture have been possible in large measure because of the combined efforts of state and federal research workers.

The heart of this partnership has always been the federal grants to the states for research. The first grants, authorized in 1887 by the Hatch Act, were only $15,000 for each state, but this small sum provided a nucleus for many stations. Even now some of the state directors look upon federal grants as "the real heart of the program of the state stations." Federal funds (amounting to $51 million for fiscal year 1967) still make up nearly one-fourth of all resources of the stations, although in some states the federal share is much smaller because of good support from their own legislatures.

Federal-grant funds have been increased several times since 1887. In 1906, the Adams Act provided an additional $15,000 to each state, and the Purnell Act of 1925 authorized an additional $60,000 for each state. The Bankhead-Jones Act of 1935 introduced two stipulations: (1) that 40 per cent of the new allotments must constitute a special research fund, to be used only for basic research; (2) that the remaining 60 per cent be distributed on the basis of rural and farm population. Thus, if a given state had 5 per cent of the total rural and farm population of the United States, it would receive 5 per cent of the funds to be allotted. The Research and Marketing Act of 1946 increased federal grants to the states on a formula basis similar to that of the Bankhead-Jones Act. To simplify administration of the various funds, both in Washington and in the states, all of the acts granting funds to the states for agricultural research were consolidated into a new Hatch Act, enacted in 1955 (Public Law 352). An excellent history of federal grant legislation is contained in *State Agricultural Experiment Stations* (Department of Agriculture Miscellaneous Publication 904), 1962.

A basic principle in all federal grants for agriculture is that the funds are to be administered by the directors of the state experiment stations. At first there was much fear that the Department of Agriculture would seek to use the grant funds to dictate how the work was to be conducted, in effect making satellites of the stations. Fortunately there is little evidence that these fears were justified. Even if the Department had such ambitions, they would have been held in check by a powerful organization of state officials created in 1887—the Association of State Universities and Land Grant Colleges. Originally known as the Association of American Agricultural Colleges and Experiment Stations, this organization has grown in scope and now maintains a staff in Washington.

Although the Department has respected the right of the stations to administer federal-grant funds, it has insisted upon a cardinal principle of the legislation: that the Secretary of Agriculture shall be responsible for approving projects to be investigated and for preventing duplication of work among the states. The first of these responsibilities is discharged by annual "inspections" of the experiment stations, usually by a team of two or more specialists. Preventing duplication is not as simple as certifying that the funds are spent on approved projects, but it appears to be working successfully. In addition to its file of all projects financed from federal funds, the Cooperative State Research Service now has files of all current projects from forty-three of the fifty states, and efforts are being made to obtain similar information from the others. Every new project at one of the stations is entered on a new card in the file. Each time a new card is added, every state doing related work is notified. Although not a guarantee against duplication, the file does provide information that is necessary for coordination.

One of the few criticisms of the federal-state research partnership is that it encourages duplication of effort. This is a tough point to prove or disprove. Nearly all scientists agree that certain kinds of replication or duplication are desirable. Response of soils to fertilizers or irrigation, for example, may vary under local conditions. Thus it is necessary that similar tests be conducted in many states, sometimes simultaneously. Officials of the Cooperative State Research Service feel that there is very little of what they call undesirable duplication in the work of the states, or in the entire federal-state research program. They cite two safeguards: the natural desire of scientists to work on new problems, and the desire of directors to take full advantage of their limited money and manpower.

Next in importance to the grant funds in the federal-state partnership is cooperative research. Unlike the grants, cooperative research is purely voluntary. It developed out of a need to stretch scarce talent and dollars and has demonstrated its value beyond any question. The great advances in plant and animal breeding, soil management, and control of insects, diseases, and weeds, are all results of cooperative state and federal research.

Cooperative research is carried out under written agreements that spell out the objectives of the study and specify what each agency will furnish in money and manpower and how the results will be published. At the beginning of fiscal year 1967, ARS had 1,263 of these written agreements with the stations.

In a typical cooperative research project, ARS will have one or more workers located at an experiment station. They will be assigned specific phases of a problem and may be working in the same laboratories or greenhouses with state men. In some cases, the addition of one or two men will round out a research team. The agency prefers to concentrate its talent in a particular field, such as wheat breeding, at a few stations rather than to assign twenty men to twenty different stations. A typical arrangement is for the Service to furnish a senior scientist and equipment, and for the state to provide office, laboratory, and field space, plus junior scientific help, often graduate students.

Many cooperative investigations center around a U.S. Department of Agriculture regional laboratory, such as the Vegetable Breeding Laboratory. With funds from the Bankhead-Jones Act of 1935, the Department built this laboratory near Charleston, South Carolina, and invited all of the states in the southeast to take part in a long-range effort to improve vegetables in the region. The states had already agreed that improved commercial vegetables was one of their greatest needs, and segments of the problem were assigned to the various states. The laboratory still serves as headquarters, and annual meetings are held to review progress and make plans for new work. Dozens of superior strains of vegetables have been developed and are now grown by farmers of the region.

In recent years, ARS has had authority to enter into contracts for research when the job can be done by an outside agency more quickly or more cheaply than by ARS. Many of these research contracts have been awarded to state experiment stations. In fiscal year 1967, approximately $5.3 million in contracts was awarded, mostly in utilization research. Since 1965, ARS has also had authority to make grants for basic research. By the beginning of 1967, it had awarded 159 such grants, totaling $8.73 million.

Problems Stem from Policies

Most of the difficulties that arise in the research partnership with the states deal with policies rather than actual working relationships. Originally, the Office of Experiment Stations was on the same level as the bureaus, and its chief reported directly to the Secretary of Agriculture. When the office became part of the Agricultural Research Administration in 1941, its chief no longer reported to the Secretary but to the administrator of the Agricultural Research Administration. When ARS was formed in 1953, the Office of Experiment Stations was abolished, and its work was taken over by two new ARS divisions—the State Experiment Stations Division and the Territorial Experiment Stations Division. The chief of the former Office of Experiment Stations had already been added to the administrator's staff in 1947 as assistant administrator for experiment stations. In 1955, his title was changed to deputy administrator.

The biggest policy dispute in many years came to a head in 1953. On the surface, it appeared to be based upon a disagreement over organizational structure and status. The big reorganization of 1953—in which the Office of Experiment Stations was abolished—never was satisfactory to the station directors. By formal resolution they had requested that the office be continued in any reorganization, and that its head report directly to the Secretary of Agriculture or to an assistant secretary. Both requests were denied when the reorganization took place. The directors finally won their battle in 1961, when the ARS State Experiment Stations Division was abolished and a new and independent agency, the Cooperative State Experiment Station Service, was created with an administrator reporting directly to the Secretary of Agriculture or an assistant secretary. (The name was changed later to Cooperative State Research Service.)

Although organizational status was the apparent cause of the policy disagreement, a look below the surface reveals that the more important cause was money—money required not for the present but for the future. Federal support for the experiment stations had increased steadily since 1941, when the Office of Experiment Stations became part of the Agricultural Research Administration, but the directors understandably felt that liberal support from Congress in the future would be more certain if their representative in the Department of Agriculture devoted full time to their cause and, as an agency head, reported to the Secretary of Agriculture and appeared before the appropriations committees of Congress. In baseball language, the directors were playing the percentages, and only the passing of time will reveal if federal appropriations to the stations from 1961 to 1981 increase faster than they did from 1941 to 1961, when the administrators of the Agricultural Research Administration and the Agricultural Research Service were their spokesmen in Washington.

Although policy differences never were allowed to interfere with the actual conduct of joint research, over-all relations between the Service and the stations were bound to improve with establishment of the Cooperative State Research Service. Now most policy matters are taken up with the latter agency, and the Agricultural Research Service is looked upon as a partner in research. Even so, effective cooperative relations require almost daily attention, and money is a continuing cause of friction.

Federal budgets are prepared many months in advance. During this period of budget preparation and approval in the executive departments and the Budget Bureau (a part of the Executive Office of the President), the strictest secrecy is enforced. Only a few people in the Service, for example, know the amounts requested for the various items in its budget, and those who know are required not to give out this information. There is ample reason for this requirement; without it the pressures to increase this or that item would create utter confusion. But because of this enforced secrecy, federal officials cannot inform state officials of budget plans or decisions during the year that the budget is in preparation. State officials may know approximately what ARS is asking for a cooperative project, but the original request of an agency may be changed considerably or even eliminated before it appears in the President's budget request to Congress.

This situation makes it very difficult for experiment station directors to plan research in cooperation with the Department of Agriculture, especially if the budget is being whittled down. For example, in fiscal years 1966 and 1967, ARS was required to reduce its budget request for research by approximately $5 million. In looking for places to cut, the agency is likely to concentrate on small projects that are poorly financed or poorly housed, or to ask that a small field station be closed. Although the state directors understand the reasoning behind the cuts, they dislike having federal support withdrawn without sufficient warning.

The President's budget for fiscal year 1967 dealt an even worse blow to the stations. It proposed a substantial cut in the Hatch Act funds appropriated to the Department for direct distribution to the states. This was the first budget proposal to reduce these funds, which the stations have been receiving for seventy-five years. The unkindest cut of all was the explanation that it was necessary to reduce the Hatch funds so that Department of Agriculture funds for specific grants to the stations could be increased. To the directors, this was a direct challenge; it said in effect that the administration lacked confidence in their ability to select suitable projects for federal funds. It was tantamount to letting the administrator of the Cooperative State Research Service select the projects, since he administers the grants for specific projects. Congress, however, ignored the President's request and restored the funds—not only for the Hatch Act but for most ARS cuts as well.

State directors are wise to the ways of Washington and are not unduly alarmed over relatively small cuts in the ARS budget that might affect their states; they are pretty sure Congress will restore those cuts. But any budget proposal to reduce the time honored Hatch Act funds is far more serious. Some of the directors are inclined to feel that someone in the Department of Agriculture could have prevented this action. Since ARS is no longer responsible for administering the Hatch Act funds, the blame is likely to fall on the Cooperative State Research Service or the Office of the Secretary.

An easy way to prevent budget difficulties between ARS and the states would be to bring the state directors into the confidence of those preparing the ARS budget or making last-minute cuts. This plan would not work, however, because the directors are free to urge members of Congress to bring pressure on the Department or the White House to restore the cuts, or make them in other states. This would nullify all the precautions taken to keep the budget confidential until presented to Congress. If the directors were offered this advance information on the condition they not disclose it to anyone, they would not accept it. They have powerful friends in Congress and do not appear to be in danger of losing their well-earned reputation for giving many dollars worth of research for every dollar invested in Hatch Act funds.

State Departments of Agriculture

Compared with the complications that arise in cooperative research, state and federal cooperation in regulatory work seems peaceful and friendly. This cooperation, like that in research, goes back a long time, and benefits from well-established patterns of operation. It also benefits from the knowledge of both parties that neither could do the job alone. It would be unrealistic and untruthful to say that no difficulties arise, but it is correct to say that ARS has no finer relations with any group than with state regulatory officials.

Some of the strongest supporters for ARS regulatory funds are state officials. They know that in most cases their campaigns would not succeed without federal funds. For this reason, they appear as witnesses at appropriations hearings in support of ARS. This is in marked contrast to state experiment station directors, who appear in behalf of the federal grant funds that come to them but seldom support requests for ARS funds.

Several principles of operation in ARS regulatory work help to explain the excellent relations with the states. First, the work is guided by mutual respect and confidence. ARS does not move into a state with a program until its officials are ready. Second, the work is based on the principle of local administration. The only conditions under which federal authorities would assume control of local activities would be the threat of a national emergency and the absence of state and local action. Third, in all instances, states are required to share fully in the cost of programs. As a rule, Congress is reluctant to provide federal funds until there is reason to believe that the states will appropriate their share.

Nevertheless, some of the difficulties in regulatory programs have arisen over failure of state legislatures to appropriate matching funds. When this happens, it is usually because the programs have become controversial in the state and lack widespread support. Through the years, the cooperative regulatory work has been tested many times by adversity, but relationships have remained excellent.

Other Federal Agencies

ARS has cooperative relationships with many agencies of the federal government. These may range from the most informal exchange of services with other agencies in the U.S. Department of Agriculture to rather large contracts from other Departments. Many processes and products developed in ARS require economic evaluation, and this service is provided by the Department's Economic Research Service on a reimbursable basis. An example of such cooperation would be the market testing of new food products developed at one of the utilization laboratories.

In some cases, the agency cooperatively plans and carries out research with other agencies. The ARS Consumer and Food Economics Division makes various consumer studies with the Economic Research Service and regularly cooperates with the Bureau of Labor Statistics of the Department of Labor in surveys of consumer spending. This division also evaluates the nutritional adequacy of the yearly food supply.

Perhaps the oldest cooperative relationship is with the Smithsonian Institution. One of the jobs of entomologists from the earliest days of the Department has been collecting insects, identifying them, and adding them to the permanent collection. The Department of Agriculture did not have suitable space for this work, and it was moved to the nearby Smithsonian Building in 1881. Through the years, maintaining the collection and adding to it has been a joint effort, with the Department supplying about 75 per cent of the staff and the Smithsonian providing the remainder of the staff and the housing. The group constitutes an international court of appeal on insect identification and provides free service to all U.S. residents and to institutions anywhere in the world. In 1965, it answered approximately 72,000 requests for identification or information. All insect control depends upon correct identification.

Knowledge of insect identification occasionally helps to fix the time of death for murder victims whose bodies are later discovered. Entomologists know what kinds of insects are attracted to animal carcasses the first week after death, the second week, and so on. By applying this knowledge, an entomologist in North Carolina once saved a man from a murder charge by certifying that the victim met death at a time when the accused was known to be in military service in a distant state.

The Department of Agriculture has a long history of doing research for the military services under contract. The most spectacular of these jobs was done during World War II and resulted in the discovery of the amazing ability of DDT to kill insects. After entomologists learned of its versatility as an insecticide, Department chemists quickly identified its components, making it possible for industry to supply it to the armed forces. An outbreak of typhus in Italy during the war was immediately brought under control by using DDT to control fleas, the carriers of the disease.

ARS entomologists made a notable contribution to the welfare of the armed forces in South Viet-Nam in 1965 by developing a leech repellant under a contract with the Department of Defense. The repellant is effective against both land and water leeches found in South Viet-Nam. This research was done at the Gainesville, Florida, laboratory, devoted to study of insects affecting man and animals, and was supported in part by the Department of Defense. In addition to doing research under contract, ARS specialists serve as advisers to the Department on a wide variety of subjects.

Under a contract from the National Aeronautical and Space Administration, ARS scientists have been developing infrared photography from spacecraft and other experimental techniques for world-wide surveys of land use and feed crops. Complex cameras and other types of sensitive instruments designed for remote observation will be used to identify areas occupied by agricultural crops, forests, and water. Equipment perfected in the Agricultural Research Service will tell not only which crops are shown in a photograph, but the condition of the crop, and whether it is threatened seriously by insects or disease. This new peaceful application of aerospace technology will be used to help other nations improve their food production; it has already been applied, with airplane equipment, in the United States.

The boundaries of an infestation of citrus black fly were immediately identified by infrared techniques, and several weeks of time were saved for ground crews.

Many ARS research projects have been financed by the Agency for International Development. One of these seeks practical ways to use high-protein crops such as soybeans, peanuts, and cottonseed as human food in areas of the world where diets are deficient in proteins. These crops are grown in many countries where animal products are scarce and diets could be greatly improved by the addition of protein from plant sources. As an example, soybean flour has 40 per cent protein, and can be made with simple equipment developed in ARS under a contract with the Agency for International Development. The big part of the job was to find ways to incorporate this product into foods that would be acceptable in those countries where more protein is already available but not being fully used.

One approach to this problem is to have scientists from some of the developing countries learn the simple processing methods in ARS laboratories and suggest ways in which high-protein flour can be used in some of the favorite foods of their countries. Foods developed under this arrangement include a peanut flour wafer, a beverage for children containing soy flour, a soft food for babies, and vegetable stews thickened with high-protein flour.

One of the most unusual jobs undertaken by the Agency for International Development has been a study of birth control in cattle that could be used in India. Officials reasoned that one way to help the food situation in India would be to limit the population of cattle that roam over the country and destroy food crops intended for human consumption. ARS scientists found that intrauterine devices made of plastic prevented reproduction in cows without serious complications. The method is quite simple, but its implementation requires the services of trained personnel. It is now under trial in India.

As part of an international study of the basic principles of reproduction, the Agricultural Research Service, under a contract with the National Institutes of Health, is investigating the effect of intrauterine devices in hogs, rats, rabbits, sheep, and water buffaloes. In contrast to the original studies with cows, the objective is to learn as much as possible about the process of reproduction in animals in the hope that the information could be used to reduce reproductive losses in all classes of livestock. General principles discovered in this work might well have human applications.

ARS also has several other research contracts with the National Institutes of Health. One of these, financed by the National Cancer Institute, is an intensive search of the world's plants for possible substances that might be useful in the control of cancer. ARS scientists collect and identify plant samples and help to evaluate test data. Other scientists working under grants from the National Cancer Institute extract chemical components from the samples and test them on laboratory animals for their effect on tumors. An interesting substance, camptothecin, was extracted in 1966 from the fruit, bark, and wood of a Chinese tree growing in the ARS Plant Introduction Station at Chico, California. Camptothecin has shown antitumor activity in tests with laboratory animals against a type of leukemia called lymphoid leukemia L-1210.

The Agricultural Research Service cooperates with other agencies of the federal government on problems created by widespread use of chemical pesticides. Although several agencies have some degree of interest, the principal ones are ARS and the Forest Service in the Department of Agriculture, the Public Health Service and the Food and Drug Administration in the Department of Health, Education, and Welfare, the Fish and Wildlife Service in the Department of the Interior, and the Department of Defense.

Cooperation is assured by a requirement from the White House that all pest control operations of the federal government be approved by the Federal Committee on Pest Control, whose members are appointed by the Secretaries of Agriculture, Interior, Defense, and Health, Education, and Welfare. The ARS member is Associate Administrator Dr. Robert J. Anderson. The committee was established when the country became alarmed over possible harm to wildlife and people from the growing use of pesticides in farming, gardening, and around the home. It has served a useful purpose, especially in bringing federal scientists together and giving them an opportunity to present their arguments for or against federal pest control programs before they are initiated.

Before the committee was appointed, each agency could decide which chemical to use in a pest control operation, the rate and frequency of application, safety precautions, and other details of the operation. Now the committee, in effect, makes these decisions by approving or rejecting plans for a control program. ARS and the Forest Service have had to modify some of their proposed plans to obtain committee approval, but when they begin an operation, they have the endorsement of those who occasionally were their most vocal critics. The committee plays an important part in coordinating federal activities in an area where there was once a lack of understanding and cooperation.

Like every federal agency, ARS has almost daily dealings with the Bureau of the Budget, a part of the Executive Office of the President. The bureau is often thought of as an arm of the President, exercising fiscal control over the entire executive branch of the government. It also operates in three general areas: budget preparation and execution, proposed legislation, and organization and management.

The bureau has a major responsibility for the annual budget. When a top figure has been decided upon for the entire federal government, each Department is given a tentative figure, referred to in the Department of Agriculture as a "ceiling." Each Secretary then breaks this down into targets, or ceilings, to guide the preparation of agency budgets. Agency budgets are cleared in each department, and department budgets are cleared in the Bureau of the Budget. Even after an appropriation bill is signed, the funds cannot be spent without approval of the bureau. This gives the President fiscal control over the entire executive branch of the government. This fiscal control operates in hundreds of items; for example, the per diem rate for employees traveling on official business.

The bureau also exercises control over legislative proposals or comments by agency officials on proposed legislation. This subject is discussed in the next chapter.

Budget Bureau controls over organization and management are not so well known as those on fiscal matters and legislation, but they are just as real. The bureau has over-all responsibility to make studies of the organization and management of any agency in the executive branch when invited to do so. A management study of ARS in 1964 by a team from the Bureau of the Budget, the Civil Service Commission, and the Department of Agriculture was quite critical of certain management practices and resulted in several changes. One was the consolidation of five field administrative divisions into three. Other recommendations were to reduce the amount of paper work in the management operations, with a consequent saving in the number of employees required.

Although not a governmental organization, the National Academy of Sciences–National Research Council plays a significant role in much governmental research. The academy is a private organization, chartered by Congress during the Civil War to advise the federal government on scientific and technical matters. Membership is by invitation and is restricted to scientists who are recognized nationally. The National Research Council was organized in 1919 to give a broader base for the activities of the Academy. Industrial firms, universities, and public research agencies may become members of the council. The organization has a staff of 700 in Washington, engaged in performing various scientific services for its members. Since it is a nonprofit organization, all services are performed at cost.

Because of its standing in the scientific community, the Na-

tional Academy of Sciences–National Research Council is frequently asked by federal agencies to plan and conduct symposia
on topics of special interest. An example is the symposium on
pesticides held in Washington in February, 1966, at the request
of the Departments of Agriculture, Interior, and Health, Education, and Welfare. Before 1965, the Agricultural Research Service did not have authority to make grants for services other than
research, but it was given this authority in Public Law 89-106
and will undoubtedly utilize the services of the National Academy of Sciences–National Research Council more often than
in former years.

ARS and Foreign Governments

In a strict sense, an agency such as ARS does not have dealings
with foreign countries; these relations are the province of the
State Department. In actual practice, however, agency officials
may play a most important role as advisers to Cabinet officers
and as negotiators with officials of equal rank in foreign countries on matters that require specialized knowledge and experience.

ARS has found itself in such situations several times in recent
years. An outbreak of foot-and-mouth disease of cattle in Mexico
was eradicated in 1954 by joint efforts of the U.S. and Mexican
governments. The two countries also cooperated to fight screwworms in a campaign that was progressing satisfactorily at the
end of 1966. ARS scientists worked side by side with employees
of the Ministry of Agriculture in Mexico, keeping constant sur-
veillance of all cattle in the northern part of that country to be
sure that every case of screwworm infestation was reported. If isolated cases threatened to spread, control measures were taken, as
explained in Chapter 4.

The Agricultural Research Service also cooperates with the
Ministry of Agriculture in Mexico in fighting several plant pests
that could be very costly to U.S. agriculture if they became estab-

lished here. One of these is the citrus black fly. By special arrangement with the Mexican government, all infested citrus groves within sixty miles of the border are sprayed to control the pest. South of this chemical control area is a biological control zone, where insect parasites are used for control. Also in cooperation with Mexico, the Mexican fruit fly is being controlled in groves near the border by the release of sterile flies—the method used to eradicate screwworms.

The Service has been conducting research on insects in Europe for many years, seeking natural enemies of pests that originated there, such as the European corn borer. ARS field stations at Paris and Rome serve as home bases for small staffs of entomologists, who collect egg masses of the parasitic or predatory insects that control the corn borer or other pest species in their natural areas. Several enemies of the corn borer have been introduced into the Corn Belt states, and are helping to keep down the numbers of this pest.

Research Grants to Foreign Institutions

Scientists in many parts of the world are carrying on research under ARS grants, with funds provided by Public Law 480 (the Agricultural Trade Development and Assistance Act of 1954). A section of this law authorizes the sale of surplus agricultural products to developing countries, with payment in foreign currencies that may not be converted into dollars but must be spent in the importing country. Some of these funds are made available to ARS for grants for research that will benefit U.S. agriculture.

Of the hundreds of grants that have been made to universities and research institutions abroad, many have been completed and the results published. One of those announced in 1965 told of a parasitic ant in Uruguay and Argentina that lives in the same mound with fire ants and prevents their spread to new territory. The parasitic ant could be useful in preventing the spread of fire ants in the southern part of the United States, where it is a serious pest of people, crops, livestock, and wildlife, as we have seen in Chapter IV.

The parasitic ant is much smaller than its host, but is much more resourceful. It does not attack the fire ant, but merely flutters its antennae to mesmerize the larger ants, who feed the parasites by regurgitating their own food. The fire ants also obligingly care for the young of the parasites along with their own. Colonies of fire ants inhabited by the parasites do not disappear but remain in a weakened condition and do not multiply rapidly or spread to new territory, as they would do under normal conditions.

Laboratory tests show that the parasitic ant will not feed on animal or plant material. Its only food is the regurgitations of fire ants. If exhaustive tests convince scientists of ARS that the parasite will not become a pest in the United States and that it can survive in the southern states, it will be imported and given a chance to control fire ants here as it does in South America.

Cooperation with Industry and Research Institutions

Cooperation with industry dates back to the early days of the scientific bureaus. Reports tell of cooperation with the livestock and dairy industry, fruit and vegetable processors, and farm machinery and fertilizer manufacturers, to mention only a few. This cooperation has continued through the years and has produced results of great value to agriculture and the nation as a whole.

The great array of fruits and vegetables found in every supermarket would not be there except for research conducted by ARS with industry support and cooperation. The work began many years ago and was concerned with maintaining quality in fruits and vegetables during the journey from centers of production to distant markets. The first work was with refrigerated railway cars and ships. Principles learned were later applied to refrigerated motor trucks and cargo planes. Scientists learned how to slow down the aging of perishables by refrigeration and treatment with gases, such as ethylene. They discovered the exact time for harvesting and the best methods of handling prior to loading. They found ways to reduce costs of refrigeration, and how to take care of produce after arrival in city markets. They even made tests to find out how often fresh vegetables should be sprinkled in the supermarket, and how much water is needed.

The widespread practice of packaging fruits and vegetables was guided by research. The holes in the plastic bag of kale or spinach allow the product inside to "breathe" and thus prolong its life. The mesh bags used for oranges permit savings in handling, but the color of the bags was chosen to make the oranges more appealing. The location of the produce area in a supermarket, the layout of the entire store, and especially the choice of items to be displayed at the check-out counter have all been decided by research.

Some of the greatest savings in food marketing have resulted from modernizing wholesale markets, which, in many of the largest U.S. cities, had become woefully inadequate. A group of ARS marketing research specialists cooperates with city officials and industry representatives in making studies of present and future needs, and makes plans for complete new wholesale market facilities, relocated in less congested areas. New markets in Atlanta, New York, and Philadelphia were planned by ARS, working with local citizens. This service is free to cities that need new markets and have plans for financing them.

Consumers benefit doubly from this kind of research. The foods are as near farm-fresh as possible, and studies show that most of the savings from more efficient marketing are passed on to consumers.

Contract research represents a relatively new kind of cooperation between ARS and other agencies. Authority to let research contracts has existed since 1946, but funds were not available for broad use of this authority until about the beginning of the

1960's. A sampling of contracts made in 1965 and 1966 for research to develop new or improved uses for farm products will be found in Appendix D.

Agricultural Research by Industry

A large amount of agricultural research is done by industry. A small share of this is pure or basic research, but most industry research is done to discover and develop new products. With a few exceptions, industry related to agriculture looks to the privately endowed institutions and public research agencies to develop information needed to explain biological, chemical, physical, and economic phenomena.

Industry's annual investment in research related to food and agriculture is estimated at about $400 million, which provides employment for approximately 12,000 scientists. About half of this research is done by processors of agricultural commodities, who give major emphasis to the development of new and improved brand-name products and to determination of consumer reaction and the market potential of their products. About one-fifth is carried on by manufacturers of machinery and equipment used in the production, processing, and distribution of farm products. Another one-fifth is done by the chemical and pharmaceutical companies that manufacture the pesticides and biological products used to control crop and livestock diseases, insects, weeds, and other pests.

VIII

ARS and Congress

The Agricultural Research Service has good relations with both houses of Congress. This relationship goes back many years, and is associated with the confidence that many people have in science and scientists. Members of the congressional committees that deal with agriculture are often from farm states and have an interest in advancing our agriculture, and they feel that one of the surest ways to do this is through research.

Another help in maintaining good relations with Congress is the fact that ARS officials do not operate at the top-policy level. In the Department of Agriculture, only the Secretary, the undersecretary, and the assistant secretaries may disagree publicly with policies established by Congress. In recent years, most of the policy disagreements between the Department and Congress have been concerned with crop adjustments, price supports, surplus disposal, and other activities associated with the farm program. ARS officials do not become identified with these programs. However, a policy dispute between the Johnson Administration and powerful interests in Congress over amounts to be spent on research did involve ARS and is discussed later in this chapter.

The top staff of ARS frequently appears before committees of Congress for consultation on proposed legislation or other matters under consideration. All such appearances by agency officials must be approved in the Secretary's office, and prepared statements must be cleared. Many of these appearances are before the House Committee on Agriculture and the Senate Committee on Agriculture and Forestry, but other committees also call on the agency for testimony. The Commerce Committee of the House, for example, asked for several appearances while considering legislation to control air and water pollution. There is constant communication of this kind between ARS and members of Congress.

ARS officials are also asked for informal visits with individual congressmen in their offices. The subject to be discussed is usually mentioned when the request is made, so that the official will have an opportunity to get the latest reports from his staff. Often such reports will include a progress report on a project in which the congressman is especially interested, such as a new laboratory scheduled for his district. Sometimes the request results from an appointment made by a congressman to see a delegation from his district, and he may wish to have an expert present to give advice on proposals made at the meeting.

Of all appearances before Congress, those before the appropriations committees are the most vital to an agency. It is here that good or poor relationships are established and the growth curve for the agency determined. ARS has been fortunate in sending articulate men to explain its needs, and for the most part they have a sympathetic audience. Historically, the House committee has been less liberal in approving increases for research than the Senate committee. For several years prior to 1956 the House committee reminded witnesses from the Agricultural Research Administration (and later from the Agricultural Research Service) of the federal deficit and asked many questions about what would be done with increased funds. Since the late 1950's, both committees have been quite generous, and ARS funds have grown steadily.

A genuine feeling of participation in the work of an agency often develops on the part of committee members, particularly the chairmen. Fortunately for ARS, the chairmen of its appropriations subcommittees in both houses have had long service on the committees. Congressman Whitten became chairman of the subcommittee in the House in 1949, and Senator Holland took over similar duties in the Senate in 1960. Senator Russell served as chairman in the Senate for many years. The seniority system guarantees that a new chairman will have served on the committee long enough to learn a great deal about an agency. The practice of giving members a preference on committee assignments also helps an agency, assuring it the opportunity of dealing with members who are interested in its work.

The regular budget hearings are held once a year, usually in late February or early March. Matters considered important enough by the administration for presentation as a supplemental item may be heard at any time convenient to the appropriations subcommittees of the House and Senate.

A Policy Conflict Involving ARS

A fundamental conflict in policy between the Johnson Administration and the conservative southern group in both houses has placed ARS in the awkward position of having to support policies that are in direct conflict with those of Congress. Because of their long tenure in office, southern congressmen hold many important committee chairmanships and this has been true of the agriculture subcommittees on appropriations in both House and Senate. Attempts to finance new programs by making cuts in some of the old and well-established activities such as research have met stubborn resistance in both houses of Congress.

The conflict embraces much more than funds for research, but it showed up in the ARS budget request for fiscal year 1966. That budget included proposed cuts in research funds of slightly more than $5 million. Part of this saving was to be made by closing about twenty field stations, most of the remainder coming from reductions at Beltsville and from cooperative research at the state experiment stations. ARS officials were given the task of making the reductions on items of lowest priority. This was done in December, 1965, shortly before the annual budget message of the President, which traditionally is sent to Congress within the first week or ten days of each new session.

Publication of the proposed budget brought protests from those interested in the work to be cut. At their budget hearings a few weeks later before the House and Senate, ARS administrators defended the cuts but had to admit under direct questioning that they were not recommended by the agency. (In testifying before a congressional committee, an agency head is expected to defend administration policy and decisions vigorously; if asked a direct question, however, he must answer it, even though the answer may upset all his previous testimony.) When the appropriations bill had been considered in committee and reported to the House and Senate, about 75 per cent of the cuts had been restored. Most of the cuts that remained in the bill were those affecting work at Beltsville.

The ARS budget situation for 1967 was similar to that of 1966, except that the rift between the administration and Congress had deepened. Reductions in research funds of almost $5.5 million were proposed. The House originally restored the entire amount, but in the final bill agreed to Senate proposals to leave a few of the proposed cuts and to add several million dollars for additional items of research. Proposed reductions in funds for regulatory work on plant and animal diseases and pest control totaled $7.8 million. Both the House and the Senate restored all of the cuts, and the Senate added another $4 million. The House concurred, and the bill passed with increases above the budget request of almost $16 million for research and $11.75 million for regulatory work.

But the same committee that had been so generous to ARS showed that they could also take money away to show their displeasure over an action of the Secretary. Because the Secretary had transferred $66,000 from ARS to the Rural Community

Development Service and $12,000 to the National Advisory Commission on Food and Fiber, the House committee reduced the ARS appropriations bill by $78,000 and said in its report (No. 1446):

These transfers were made from funds authorized by the Congress last year for specific research purposes. Through the years the Committee has relied upon officials of the Department to keep it informed in advance of proposed shifts in the use of funds specifically authorized by the Congress for certain purposes. . . . Since this agency was able to operate during the fiscal year without the funds which were transferred for other uses, they have been eliminated for the coming fiscal year.

The message was clear: the House committee did not like to have research funds used for other purposes. The Secretary has the legal authority to make such transfers between agencies, and the ARS administrator has similar authority to transfer funds within the Agricultural Research Service, but the agency always notifies the committee of proposed transfers. The committee report then severely criticized the Administration for proposing to close several small field stations—some of which had also been on the list to be closed the year before. Of all places to effect savings, the report said, the executive branch had made just about the worst possible choice. Then becoming more specific, the report pointed out that

A reduction of $5,401,300 is proposed in research activities of the ARS. This would seriously impair valuable research in nearly every phase of agriculture, including costs of production, control of insects and diseases, soil and water conservation, agricultural engineering, commodity utilization, human nutrition, and marketing efficiency. Under this reduction, less research attention would be given to many of the Nation's important food crops, the supplies of some of which are at low levels at present, including wheat, corn, grain sorghums, rice, sugar cane, sugar beets, fruits and vegetables, and livestock. Important research work at 24 locations throughout the country would be eliminated during the current year. The proposed cut would also terminate or curtail essential research activities at 70 additional locations in nearly every area of the Nation during the fiscal year 1967.

Although it is recognized that insects and diseases decrease the supply and increase the cost of food, the elimination or reduction of certain pest control activities is proposed. While these pests, which infest the soil and destroy crops, are already doing billions of dollars of damage annually on millions of acres of land, the budget would reduce or terminate efforts to prevent their spread to other areas of the country.

What the report did not say, but what is generally known to those who are involved in the battle of the field stations, is that the proposed cuts in the budget represented the lowest priorities in ARS research. The selection of items to be cut was made by ARS officials, who would have been willing to give up $1 million or more in small and inefficient operations. They know from experience that making up these lists of cuts is an exercise in futility, but they do it because they have no choice. If—however remote the possibility—the entire list of proposed cuts should be dropped from the appropriations act, it would cause no great damage to the total research program.

Why, then, do the House and Senate committees restore most of the cuts if they know the facts and understand the background? The answer is that they do know the facts, they do understand the background, but they also know and understand politics. The chairmen of both committees are able men, who feel that they are responsible to the people of the United States to see that funds are provided for research and other programs necessary to guarantee abundant supplies of food and fiber. To do this, they must have the votes necessary to pass the agricultural appropriations bill every year and the votes are no longer guaranteed by a "farm bloc" in Congress. Less than 8 per cent of the people now are farmers, and redistricting of congressional districts has removed the advantage once enjoyed by farm and rural areas.

So the decisions in Congress are based upon the hard reality of getting enough votes to do what the members of the committee feel is necessary for the welfare of the country. Even if the proposed cuts do represent the lowest priorities in research, it would be foolhardy to antagonize 70 congressmen (representing the 70 districts mentioned in the committee report) whose votes are needed when the committee presents its recommendations to the House. That is the way the House committee looks at the annual battle of the field stations. The Senate committee takes a more relaxed attitude, but it arrives at the same conclusion.

In signing the bill for 1967, President Lyndon Johnson called attention to the increases beyond his budget request and said he would not allow this additional money to be spent. The President has the power to do this if he thinks it wise.

The strong congressional support enjoyed by ARS and other research agencies often carries a price tag. Congressmen who serve on appropriations committees often feel a responsibility to defend the agency against all critics. It is understandable, therefore, if their support is tinged at times with paternalism. ARS has had this experience, but it is only a minor irritation that must be endured.

This paternalistic relationship is revealed in the reports of both House and Senate appropriations subcommittees for the fiscal year 1967. Each committee gives specific directions to the ARS administrator on the spending of certain funds. This would not be unusual except that for several years both subcommittees have recommended, and both houses of Congress have passed, bills appropriating large sums to ARS under very broad language that shows confidence in the judgment and competence of the ARS administrator. The bill for 1967 reads, in part, as follows:

> Research: For research and demonstrations of the production and utilization of agricultural products, agricultural marketing and distribution, not otherwise provided for, home economics or nutrition and consumer use of agricultural and associated prod-

ucts, and related research and services, and for acquisition of land by donation, exchange, or purchase at a nominal cost not to exceed $100; $123,844,600, and in addition not to exceed $25,000,000 from funds available under section 32 of the Act of August 24, 1933, pursuant to Public Law 88-250 shall be transferred to and merged with this appropriation.

The amount in the 1967 appropriation for research represented an increase of almost $16 million above the President's budget, and almost $5 million more than ARS received in 1966. The amount for regulatory activities was $81.5 million, an increase of approximately $12 million above the budget, and $6 million above 1966. With this kind of treatment by Congress, even with a few specific directives on certain projects, it would be difficult to see how ARS could improve its congressional relations.

Congressional Investigations

The Agricultural Research Service has never been the subject of a full-dress congressional investigation, although there have been several investigations by the appropriations committee of the House dealing with the expenditures of funds. One of the most drastic investigations took place in 1949, before ARS came into existence, on the use of funds in the grasshopper control program carried on by the former Bureau of Entomology and Plant Quarantine.

After spending several weeks in the area where the campaign was in progress, the investigators charged the bureau with inefficient use of funds. Their charges were based upon discovery of excess equipment and supplies, inefficient use of personnel, and excessive rates for rental of airplanes. Although the bureau was at fault on several counts, it was caught in a change-over in control methods from wet bait put out by ground equipment, to dry bait put out by planes, and it had on hand large quantities of materials used in preparing the wet bait. The House hearings for the bureau in 1951 show how difficult it can be for a government official to explain what appears to be poor management of public funds. As a result of this investigation, there was a reorganization of the division responsible for the grasshopper program.

The question of what constitutes an adequate supply of publications was the subject of an investigation in 1964 by the General Accounting Office, an agency that reports to Congress and whose purpose is to see that federal funds are properly spent. The investigation brought out some facts that were embarrassing to Department of Agriculture agencies, including ARS, but did not result in any major change in policies or practices.

The specific objective of this investigation was to learn if storage space for publications was used efficiently. Several instances of what appeared to be excessive or even unneeded supplies of publications were discovered by the investigators. These were duly reported, and the reports made interesting newspaper stories for the Washington papers. In one case, a million copies of a small folder used in one of the animal disease eradication campaigns were discovered in a haymow at Beltsville. In another case, a "forgotten" cache of publications was found in the subbasement of the South Agriculture Building in Washington. The Agricultural Research Service insisted that these publications were neither hidden in the barn nor forgotten in the subbasement, and that all would eventually be used as originally intended. A check two years later revealed that they had been used.

The reason for ordering large quantities of publications is the savings in cost per copy. If the cost of a small campaign folder were $100 for the first 100,000 copies, the cost for subsequent lots would be only a small fraction of that amount. This opportunity to save on printing charges is an incentive to order larger quantities than may be needed immediately, with the result that some must be held in storage. If the investigators had known where to look they might have found additional publications at

Beltsville. ARS scientists, like most others, often have a small supply of old and little-used technical publications carefully put away to take care of meritorious requests, such as those from libraries or scientists in foreign countries.

A congressional investigation may be touched off in various ways. In 1955, the House subappropriations committee learned that the agency had a man on its staff who was writing a book on orchids of Guatamala. That was enough to start an investigation, which not only confirmed the orchid report but also revealed that another employee was completing a book on the flora of Dominica (one of the Windward Islands in the Caribbean). The committee thought this was getting pretty far from farming, so its investigators searched the central file of all ARS projects to see what else was going on that they might question.

At the House hearings for 1956, several members of the committee took turns asking for explanations. The facts were that both of the authors referred to were assigned to activities having nothing to do with their publications, that both publications were practically complete when the scientists were recruited by ARS and that most of the time spent on the books had been in final preparation and reading proof. Both authors had requested an opportunity to complete their publications as a condition of their employment, and this had been granted by their supervisor, who felt that ARS was justified in helping, in this small way, to advance the knowledge of plants in Latin America and the Caribbean, an area of great interest to U.S. plant explorers. Despite valiant efforts of the administrator to defend what his subordinates had done (without his knowledge), he was severely reprimanded by the committee.

Appropriations for Research Facilities

In spite of occasional troubles on Capitol Hill, ARS has had strong support from Congress in recent years, especially since about 1960. This fact is illustrated by the generous appropriations for new facilities in fiscal year 1967. Appropriations, providing nearly $12 million for construction of new laboratories and other facilities at fifteen locations throughout the country, were allocated as follows:

1. $700,000 to expand poultry husbandry research for climatic conditions of the Southwest.

2. $100,000 to provide modern laboratory and office space for the sugar cane research station.

3. $175,000 to provide modern greenhouses at the Southern Piedmont Research Center, near the University of Georgia at Athens.

4. $3,160,000 to provide facilities for research on control of insects in stored grain and on drying, conditioning, and handling grain, and for engineering research on efficient layout and work methods for these operations.

5. $250,000 to modernize greenhouses used in research on ornamental plants at the Agricultural Research Center.

6. $600,000 to expand facilities for research on cereal diseases, in cooperation with the University of Minnesota.

7. $935,000 to expand facilities of the National Sedimentation Laboratory.

8. $481,000 to provide modern facilities for research on range livestock.

9. $3,450,000 to begin construction of facilities at the new Meat Animal Research Center.

10. $583,000 to establish a new field station for nutrition and consumer economics research.

11. $380,000 to conduct soil and water conservation research, Pendleton, Oregon.

12. $360,000 to expand facilities for research at the Regional Pasture Research Laboratory.

13. $25,000 to make a feasibility study for a soil and water conservation research center.

14. $325,000 to expand facilities for soil and water research, Bushland, Texas.

15. $345,000 to enlarge facilities for research on barley.

IX

Controversies and Conflicts

The most crucial controversy involving ARS broke in the summer of 1962, with a blistering indictment of the widespread use of chemicals to control insects, animal and plant diseases, and weeds. The Service is responsible for research on pesticides, recommendations for their use, and enforcement of a law designed to assure their safety and effectiveness. In addition it is a large user of pesticides in insect control programs. Thus ARS was put on the defensive as never before.

Although there was a growing anxiety over possible dangers from pesticides, the immediate cause of this tidal wave of criticism was Rachel Carson's book *Silent Spring*. On June 16, 1962, the first installment of *Silent Spring* appeared in *The New Yorker* in advance of book publication, giving warning that the Department of Agriculture, particularly ARS, was headed for trouble. Before the book was published in the fall of 1962, it had been chosen as book of the month by one of the large mail-order book clubs; upon publication, it became a best seller and remained on the list of best sellers for several months.

The author stated near the beginning of *Silent Spring* (page 12) that "we have put poisonous and biologically potent chemicals indiscriminately into the hands of persons largely or wholly ignorant of their potentials for harm." On the next page she added that "we have allowed these chemicals to be used with little or no advance investigation of their effect on soil, water, wildlife, and man himself."

Such statements from a well-known author and biologist were bound to attract attention, and ARS officials felt that those statements were directed straight at them. The events leading up to these charges, the reports and hearings that followed, and the response of the federal government, are all related in this chapter. This is not an attempt to present all the evidence or to arrive at any conclusions regarding the great debate on pesticides. This chapter deals, instead, with an extremely difficult period in the life of a government agency, and, it is hoped, will provide material for a case study of democratic government in action.

Background of the Controversy

Man has had to compete with insects for his food supply ever since he settled down and began planting crops and raising livestock. One of his earliest weapons used against these pests was sulphur. A century ago, he discovered that compounds of arsenic were effective, as were nicotine and pyrethrum, both derived from plants. Calcium arsenate was developed in 1912 to fight cotton boll weevils, and lead arsenate was widely used to control fruit insects. In the 1920's, there was a big scare over use of arsenic compounds, and the Department of Agriculture sought to develop new organic pesticides such as rotenone, and to improve some of the old ones such as pyrethrum. Dilute oil sprays were tested and used as substitutes for lead arsenate on apples and other tree fruits. To add to their other woes, fruit growers found that insects were developing resistance to lead arsenate, and increasingly larger amounts were required to kill them.

That was the situation at the beginning of World War II. The Department of Agriculture, with funds from the Army, was searching for insecticides that could be used safely by troops to kill lice, fleas, mosquitoes, and other insects that spread human diseases. A laboratory at Orlando, Florida, was devoting full time to this effort and had already produced some effective compounds that served as insect repellants when applied to the hands, face, and clothing.

In 1942, the laboratory received a batch of chemicals for testing. Among them was one from the firm of J. R. Geigy of Basel, Switzerland, that had been effective against Colorado potato beetles. Its chemical identity was unknown, but it was given a number and put through the usual screening tests for chemicals designed to kill insects that bother man. Almost immediately it showed its superiority over the other chemicals being tested. One of its most remarkable qualities was its persistence. When applied to clothing, it protected man from typhus-carrying lice for several weeks. It even killed insects that merely walked over a surface that had been treated with the preparation. It remained active for months, and this fact suggested to the scientists the possibility of controlling mosquitoes by using this chemical as a spray inside tents and other places where insects could come in contact with it.

Department chemists quickly analyzed the new compound and found that its constituents were chlorine, carbon, and hydrogen, and determined its structure. They made samples in their laboratories, and the chemical industry was soon manufacturing enough under license from the Geigy Company to provide protection to our armed forces against insect carriers of disease. After the war, this new compound was evaluated by federal and state entomologists, and was soon made available to farmers and gardeners, who hailed it as the most amazing insecticide they had ever used.

That, in brief, is how DDT came to the United States. It was first described in 1874, but its value as an insecticide was first discovered in 1939 by Paul Muller, an employee of Geigy, who later received a Nobel prize for his discovery.

Amazing Properties of New Chemicals

Research at Orlando touched off experiments with DDT all over the country as soon as supplies became available. The insecticide proved to be effective against hundreds of insect pests. It opened a new era in insect control—the era of synthetic insecticides. Although many additional chemicals are now available, DDT is still the most widely used, and the problems associated with its use will illustrate the difficult position of ARS in the pesticides debate.

To understand the issues in this debate it is necessary to keep in mind the tremendous superiority of DDT and the other new insecticides over the old chemicals. Crop yields went up, quality of many crops was greatly improved by the absence of insect damage, and production costs went down. It is easy to see why farmers, extension workers, research entomologists, and public health officials became enthusiastic over the new insect killers. For the first time in history, man had an effective weapon against insect carriers of some of his most dread diseases.

With the new organic insecticides came a new family of chemicals to kill weeds. We have already seen that the most widely used of these herbicides, 2,4-D, kills most broad-leafed plants by speeding up their metabolism so much that they cannot manufacture food as fast as they use it. Other herbicides work on different principles, but almost all are selective; they kill one type of plant without harming other plants. Since 1950, farmers have come to depend upon the new herbicides as much as upon the new insecticides. In an experiment with strawberries, the cost of weed control with hand labor was $200 an acre; with herbicides the cost was reduced to $30. In another test, chopping cotton by hand to control weeds cost $24 an acre; control with herbicides cost $8.

At the same time new chemicals became available for better control of plant and animal diseases. Chemicals known as growth regulators prevented apples from dropping off the trees before maturity, and made many ornamental plants grow short or tall as desired. A type of growth regulator, known as a defoliant, made plants shed their leaves; it was used to defoliate fields of cotton so that mechanical pickers would not pick the leaves along with the cotton.

Many other new chemicals that do equally useful jobs on farms and ranches came into use between 1945 and 1965. They are not discussed here because they did not play a major role in the great debate over pesticides. *Protecting Our Food*, the 1966 Yearbook of Agriculture, gives concise descriptions of the chemicals used in the production and processing of food.

Insects Develop Resistance

Despite its bright promise to agriculture, the new age of chemicals was headed for trouble from its beginning. Fruit growers soon discovered that orchards sprayed with DDT to control codling moths became infested wth spider mites, tiny creatures that suck the juices of plants and often cause severe injury. The mites had been present in orchards all along, but natural enemies had been holding them in check. For some reason the mites are not bothered by DDT, even though it kills their natural enemies along with the codling moths, which are responsible for wormy apples. The next bad news was that several species of insects were developing resistance to DDT. This created a demand for more and more new compounds, but some insects developed resistance to the newer compounds. It was still a war between man and nature, with victory very much in doubt.

But that was not all. The very quality of DDT that made it so useful—its persistence—made scientists wonder how long it would leave residues in soil and water, and in crops to be eaten by farm animals or man. Toxicologists had discovered that DDT was stored in the fatty tissue of animals that consumed feeds containing residues and that it could be absorbed through the skin and accumulated in the body of the animal. The fact that millions of soldiers had used it in powder form on their bodies without harm did not satisfy those who were fearful that such residues could be harmful to man or animals if consumed over long periods. They pointed out that for agricultural use DDT was usually dissolved in oil, and could be readily absorbed through the skin. Toxicologists had made experiments that showed no apparent injury to a group of human volunteers who consumed very small quantities for periods ranging up to eighteen months. But such experiments would not answer the questions of possible long-term effects of DDT residues present in the tissues of man and animals. Toxicologists and pharmacologists of health agencies were not satisfied with the information at hand. Special study committees were appointed by the National Academy of Sciences to consider the problem of pesticidal residues in foods.

Concern Over Residues

ARS entomologists and chemists shared the concern of the toxicologists about the possible harmful residues of the new chemicals. Hearings before the House Appropriations Subcommittee for 1950 and later years testified to that concern. Scientists began studies with the resources at their disposal, but they could not begin to obtain all the information needed to answer the questions that were being asked about residues of the new pesticides. In the hearings of the House Appropriations Subcommittee for fiscal year 1951, held January 23, 1950, for example, there are five pages of discussions of the need for more information on the potentially harmful effects of insecticides, and a request for a $93,000 increase to expand research. Such requests, including funds for more research on biological control of insects, were repeated every year by the research workers, and some moderate increases were approved, but the requests were nearly always scaled down by the administration and by Congress. The substantial sums required for the extremely complex and difficult task of appraising the effects of pesticide residues in the environment had to wait until the nation had become thoroughly alarmed.

In the meantime, reports of dead birds, dead fish, and other wildlife became more frequent, following large-scale spray operations against various insects. Owners of private homes in sprayed areas protested to newspapers and members of Congress that their rights were violated when DDT was sprayed on their property without their consent. A court case against the Secretary of Agriculture and the State of New York was dismissed, but it received much publicity. Nature lovers and conservationists demanded that state and federal governments stop all spray programs using DDT and other persistent insecticides. Other suits were filed in court by farmers whose crops were damaged by the drifting of dust used to kill weeds on adjacent farms. Because of the newspaper coverage of these events, many who did not usually keep up with agricultural affairs were made aware of the controversy, and various groups joined in condemning the new chemicals.

While these events were taking place, the Agricultural Research Service was cooperating with several states in campaigns against such pests as gypsy moths in the Northeast, Japanese beetles in the Middle West, grasshoppers in the West, and fire ants in the South. Although biological agents were used against gypsy moths and Japanese beetles, the principal weapon in all cases was DDT or another effective chemical. The reason for the choice of weapons was simple: the biological agents were limited in their effectiveness and could not prevent the spread of the pests to new areas, and the older chemicals were far less effective and more expensive than the new ones.

Both the research staff of ARS and the regulatory staff were involved. The research staff was responsible for guiding the regulatory staff in the choice and rate of application of chemicals used, but the research responsibility went far beyond that; in cooperation with the state experiment stations and the chemical industry, ARS scientists were learning how farmers could use the new pesticides to fight insects, diseases, and weeds. Need for such information led to the publication each year of a Department of Agriculture handbook giving recommended methods of pest control. This publication is considered the last word on the subject and is used freely by the states and grower associations in making up their own lists of recommendations for farmers, gardeners, and homeowners. Methods are suggested for controlling hundreds of crop and livestock pests, and most of these recommendations rely on the new chemicals. To say that ARS was deeply involved in pesticide usage in the United States would be an understatement. The agency practically called the signals. Yet in spite of growing opposition, until the summer of 1962, no one who commanded national attention and respect had suggested that this agency of dedicated career scientists was derelict in exercising its responsibility on pesticides. This situation was soon to change; *Silent Spring* was already in press.

Silent Spring *Indicts ARS*

The first impact of *Silent Spring* was a general indictment by the urban press of those in the state experiment stations and the U.S. Department of Agriculture who had any responsibility for pesticides: The research staff should have spent more effort finding substitutes for the potent chemicals. The regulatory staff should have been more critical in registering new chemicals and using them in large scale operations. The administrator of ARS (by inference) was lax in allowing his agency to go so far afield, and the Secretary of Agriculture (also by inference) was responsible for all the shortcomings of his department. And so it went.

Silent Spring was acclaimed by most book reviewers. It was plainly a book with a message. The message was that man was poisoning his environment and possibly sowing the seeds of his own destruction through use of the new and potentially dangerous pesticides. Its author was a gifted writer as well as a naturalist trained in biology, and she wrote beautifully and convincingly. The "List of Principal Sources" at the end of the book covers fifty-five pages. To many reviewers, this list alone was proof of authenticity for every statement in the book.

The author told a special committee of Congress that she had spent four years collecting source material and writing the book. To many readers, the book had all the earmarks of a work of scholarship, plus complete dedication to a cause with which most people were in accord. The author believed that widespread use of modern pesticides was polluting our air and water, poisoning our soils and many of the food crops grown on them, killing fish and wildlife, and endangering man through the gradual build-up of toxic substances in vital organs of the body. She also believed that manufacturers of pesticides were too little concerned with the effects of their products, and that agricultural scientists were so intoxicated with a new sense of power over nature that they were insensitive to the harm that might result. These fears were eloquently set forth, with documentation to convince most readers that the country faced a crisis. The theme of the book was echoed and re-echoed across the land, coupled with inferences of incompetence in the Department of Agriculture, which meant the Agricultural Research Service.

The agency's first reaction was to defend itself. A careful scrutiny of the book was made by scientists, who found many questionable points. They did not accept some of the sources quoted as authoritative, and they felt that the author had drawn sweeping conclusions from insufficient evidence. To many in ARS, the book seemed more of an appeal to the emotions than a well-balanced treatment of the subject. They felt that it failed to take into account the many frustrations involved in producing food for a people who demanded an abundance of high-quality products, free of blemishes caused by insects and diseases.

The official position of the Department, as set forth in a statement by the Secretary, was that the author of *Silent Spring* had performed a useful service by arousing the nation to an impending danger. The Department agreed that more knowledge was needed to deal with the problem of residues and asserted that it would seek funds to expand its research and law enforcement activities. Public expressions by employees of the Department of Agriculture were expected to conform to this policy statement.

To add to the frustrations of research, regulatory, and extension workers, there were suggestions in the press and elsewhere that DDT and all other persistent pesticides should be outlawed immediately.

Agricultural scientists in the states were free to express their opinions and many of them pointed out that there was no medical record of anyone who had been harmed by proper use of pesticides. They warned that a ban on the use of DDT and other persistent pesticides would endanger the nation's food supply. They were joined by research people in industry, some of whom were employed by the chemical companies that manufactured pesticides.

In addition to the Department of Agriculture, three other departments of the federal government have responsibilities relating to pesticides. The Food and Drug Administration of the Department of Health, Education, and Welfare cooperates with the ARS Pesticides Regulation Division in the registration of pesticides as part of its broad responsibility for the safety of U.S. food; the Public Health Service of the same department cooperates with states to control flies, mosquitoes, and other insects that spread diseases of humans; the Fish and Wildlife Service of the Department of the Interior is concerned with protecting wildlife; and the Defense Department uses pesticides on a large scale, when necessary, to protect the armed services.

This broad involvement of the federal government, with each department ready and willing to defend its actions and to protect its sphere of influence, produced an ideal environment for conflicts among the agencies involved. Alert reporters took advantage of every incident involving pesticides to interview officials of the various departments in the hope of uncovering newsworthy items, such as conflicting policy or practices and lack of coordination. Because the Department of Defense and the Public Health Service were using pesticides to protect people, rather than crops or livestock, they were spared much of the criticism heaped upon the Department of Agriculture. The Fish and Wildlife Service was portrayed in a heroic light, engaged only in protecting the helpless creatures of nature. The Food and Drug Administration was blamed for not enforcing the pure food law more strictly, but the principal criticism was aimed at the Department of Agriculture.

The Pesticide Hearings

A public controversy that involves four departments of the federal government cannot be ignored by the White House. Accordingly, President John F. Kennedy requested his Science Advisory Committee to make a study of the subject. The committee asked each department for an exhaustive statement giving detailed information on all activities related to pesticides. As always happens in such cases, the time allowed for this work seemed unreasonably short. The statements were later published as Appendixes I and II to Part 1 of the pesticides hearings conducted by the Senate Subcommittee on Reorganization and International Organizations; the Department of Agriculture statement filled 741 printed pages. The report of the Science Advisory Committee, "Use of Pesticides," was made public on May 15, 1963, with a Foreword by the President, stating that he had already requested the responsible agencies to implement the report's recommendations.

The report recommended a general tightening of federal controls over pesticides, closer coordination among the three departments of government most concerned, and a monitoring program to check residues in air, water, soil, man, fish, and wildlife. Of special interest to ARS was the recommendation that the Department of the Interior share responsibility in the registration of pesticides, as well as recommendations for gradual elimination of DDT and other persistent pesticides, for establishing a monitoring program, for more emphasis on research in all departments (except Defense), and for a public information program urging all users of pesticides to follow label instructions carefully.

The recommendations on monitoring and public information were already in effect in the Agricultural Research Service. Recommendations for more research were most welcome, but those on registration and DDT bothered ARS. Registration of pesticides was a thankless job under any conditions, but to have responsibility shared by two departments seemed to be an open invitation to disagreement and delay. The suggestion that DDT no longer be used was a reasonable goal for the future, but ARS officials were worried over the prospect of an edict that would outlaw DDT before suitable substitutes could be developed. In conformance with governmental policy, the agency could not express its reservations on these recommendations to anyone except the Secretary of Agriculture.

Although there was no specific recommendation on the point, the report challenged the concept of pest eradication, a cardinal point in Department of Agriculture pest control operations since 1887. The Department has always contended that it was far cheaper to eradicate a newly introduced pest than for farmers to spend money every year on large quantities of insecticides to control it. Although the language of the report showed that the committee was thinking primarily of insects, ARS was nevertheless concerned that it might be forced to abandon what had proved to be the best way to deal with many pests including insects. Congress has consistently supported ARS in its policy of eradication whenever possible.

The Senate took note of the nation-wide interest in pesticides, including the interest shown by the White House, and passed a resolution calling for its Committee on Government Operations to hold hearings on coordination among federal agencies concerned with environmental hazards. The task was assigned to the Subcommittee on Reorganization and International Organizations. The hearings began on May 16, 1963, and were presided over by Senator Abraham A. Ribicoff of Connecticut. Although the hearings eventually covered a much broader field, so far as ARS was concerned, they were "pesticide hearings."

The Ribicoff committee heard dozens of witnesses from industry, universities, and government, beginning with Dr. Jerome B. Wiesner, Special Assistant to the President for Science and Technology. It heard from Secretary of the Interior Stewart L. Udall, Secretary of Agriculture Orville L. Freeman, Secretary of Health, Education, and Welfare Anthony J. Celebrezze, and several of their aides. It also heard from Miss Carson and representatives of industry. All government witnesses agreed that pesticides were necessary for food production, that much more knowledge was necessary before man could be completely sure that the use of pesticides posed no risk, and that the way to get this assurance was through research. They also agreed that certain changes were needed in legislation to tighten control of the interstate sale of pesticides and to redefine tolerances of residues in food or feed crops for the proper enforcement of the food and drug laws. Miss Carson sought to clarify her position by admitting that pesticides were necessary in some cases, but she felt that the Department of Agriculture had carried out some spray programs without sufficient justification. The industry representatives stressed the value of pesticides, agreeing to some of the recommendations of the report of the President's committee and objecting vigorously to others.

The hearings went on intermittently for fifteen months, and ARS officials were not able to forget the subject for a single day of that time. They were busy answering their telephones and preparing reports for the White House, the Congress, or the Secretary. During this period an amendment to the Insecticides, Fungicides, and Rodenticides Act was enacted that prohibited registration of a pesticide "under protest," a legal device that had enabled manufacturers, under the original law, to place a product on the market even though it did not meet all requirements for registration. The Agricultural Research Service made the mistake of withholding from the public the names of such products on the ground that this was confidential information that should not be given to competitors. Senator Ribicoff threatened to reveal the names of these products on the floor of the Senate, and ARS quickly changed its policy, on orders from the Secretary of Agriculture. When the list was made public, it contained twenty-seven products, out of a total of nearly 60,000 registered.

Another tactical error of ARS had been its failure to make public announcement of products seized because they were being sold illegally. In the past, there had been very little interest in such announcements, but information workers decided it would be wise to issue such releases anyhow, as a defensive move. There was no objection other than "we've never done it before," so ARS began announcing seizures, as the Food and Drug Administration had done for many years.

The transcript of the hearings, when published, comprised sixteen volumes, containing 3,747 pages. Following the usual practice, the committee had a staff of experts digest this great mass of material and prepare a report ("Pesticides and Public Policy," Senate Report 1379), which gave excellent coverage of the hearings.* Although claiming that the contribution of pesticides to an expanded food supply and to public health "has been so immense as to virtually defy comprehension," the report

---

* Those interested in all the details of congressional hearings, such as the pesticide hearings, will find no substitute for the transcript, but others will find that the reports usually give complete summaries of what took place. Copies of congressional documents will be found in most college and university libraries and in public libraries of large cities. Those who need reports for extended use may often obtain copies from committee chairmen. When this is not possible, the reports or complete transcripts can usually be purchased from the Superintendent of Documents, U.S. Government Printing Office, Washington, D.C., 20402. In the case of the pesticide hearings, however, the committee staff underestimated the demand for the report and did not suggest that the Government Printing Office print copies for sale.

also stated that "pesticides can constitute a certain health hazard and have a potential for causing undesirable changes in certain phases of our natural environment."

In summarizing the issues in the hearings, the report reached the conclusion "that no significant human health hazard exists today" but that this is no proof against health hazards of the future. Another conclusion was that research should seek to discover "weaknesses of pests leading to new control methods; effects on non-target organisms; consequences of environmental manipulation; and improved agricultural practice." On the subject of biological control of insects the report stated that "the data of the hearings do not support this approach as a panacea," and that all methods of control should be explored. This was exactly what ARS had been practicing for many years.

One of the significant sections of the report dealt with effects of the hearings. Some of the more important effects were: all agencies involved reviewed their responsibilities for pesticides; agency coordination was greatly strengthened by creation of the Federal Committee on Pest Control, which was given much broader authority than the Federal Pest Control Review Board, which it replaced; new laws were enacted, and regulations were established to give greater protection to users of pesticides.

The committee made several recommendations. Those that applied to the Agricultural Research Service were: that Congress enact legislation giving the Department of Agriculture authority to inspect all pesticide manufacturing or formulating plants, sample their products, and enforce good operating practices in disposal of waste products and used containers (to prevent contamination of streams and water supplies); that Congress provide legislative authority for the activities of the Federal Committee on Pest Control; and that the executive branch improve coordination of research among federal agencies by requiring them to register their programs with the Science Information Exchange of the Smithsonian Institution.

Aftermath of the Hearings

While the hearings were in progress, it was commonly believed in ARS that if the agency could survive the criticism, it would end up with a big increase in funds for research, and that is exactly what happened. Aside from the changes in registration of pesticides and strengthening of coordination through the Federal Committee on Pest Control, the really big thing that came from the hearings was more money for research. The hearings had been so complex, with so many arguments that could not be proved or disproved, that there were relatively few points on which all could agree. Two such points were the need for better coordination and the need for more research.

Although the agency had been asking for several years for increases in research to discover improved methods of pest control that would avoid residues, the amounts received had been far below those requested. About 1960, ARS began laying plans to establish large laboratories in Arizona, Georgia, Florida, Missouri, Mississippi, North Dakota, South Dakota, and Texas. (Several members of the congressional appropriations committees were residents of those states.)

The pesticide hearings had not been completed when, early in 1964, ARS testified at its budget hearings for fiscal year 1965. The budget sent up by the President called for an increase of nearly $16 million for research to discover ways to control pests that would avoid harmful residues, compared to an increase of $500,000 a year earlier. This showed that the White House had got the message of the hearings. The Department of Agriculture had got the message, too, and had requested large increases. Even though the request had been scaled down between Beltsville and the White House, there was always the possibility that the Senate might increase it.

The budget was still pending in the House when President

Johnson sent up a budget amendment, requesting almost $30 million of additional funds for the Departments concerned with pesticides. Congress promptly appropriated most of the sum requested, and the Agricultural Research Service received $14.5 million, mostly for research. Thus the goal of developing pest controls without harmful residues zoomed in value from a $500,000 increase in 1964 to a $30 million increase one year later. To some of the scientists, it was almost unbelievable—to have enough new money to do many of the things they had been wanting to do for years. A good share of the additional money was for building new laboratories in the states, so the actual operating increases were not as large as the over-all figures suggest. Even so, the logjam on pesticide research was broken.

Other logjams began to break up about the same time. The hearings had given an opportunity for many people to have their say. Discovery of large masses of dead fish in the lower Mississippi reopened the argument that agricultural use of pesticides was responsible, but even this controversy died down when a team of federal investigators reported that pesticide wastes from one or more chemical plants along the river could have been the major source of the pesticides found in river water. (The precise cause of the massive fish kills had not been determined at the end of 1966.)

One of the responses of ARS to the hearings was to intensify its monitoring of the use of pesticides. Results of the first year of follow-up studies in areas where pesticides had been used heavily showed that residues were generally present at very low levels in soils, water, aquatic life, wildlife, and domestic animals. Even so, the significance of even a trace of these residues in terms of long-range hazards to man has not yet been fully determined. The number of studies was later increased, and with more research funds available, the Department of Health, Education, and Welfare and the Department of the Interior became participants in the program, conducting monitoring studies of areas where little or no pesticides had been used.

Another response of ARS was to intensify its efforts to inform the general public that pesticides were potential hazards and must be used according to label instructions. The states and industry conducted similar educational programs. The press, radio, and television industry gave good support. With the cooperation of the Extension Service, several million copies of a leaflet on this subject were distributed, and several popular publications were prepared in ARS for wide distribution to specialized audiences, such as dairymen, home gardeners, and householders.

An additional response was the continuous re-evaluation of all pest control programs. In some cases smaller amounts of pesticides, were used, as research showed the amounts could be cut. Fortunately, the ARS methods improvement group discovered a bait control for fire ants that was harmless to other forms of life, and the low-volume sprays of some of the non-persistent insecticides proved to be effective against grasshoppers, boll weevils, and other insects previously controlled with persistent chemicals.

The simple expedient of making public announcements of all "good" news undoubtedly helped to restore ARS to the good graces of many people within, as well as outside, the government. Every interesting discovery that held out hope for any of the biological control methods was written up. So was every progress report on sterilizing insects, and on the monitoring studies. Research on conventional pesticides went ahead, but shifting of emphasis in research to the control methods that posed no residue problems was emphasized in reporting research to the public.

About the time the pesticide hearings were drawing to a close, in the summer of 1964, the Agriculture Subcommittee of the House Appropriations Committee asked its staff to make an investigation on certain aspects of pesticides. The subcommittee felt that the farmers of the country, the U.S. Department of Agriculture, and the agricultural colleges and universities had been subjected to unfair and unsupportable criticism in the pesticides debate. Its investigation attempted, therefore, to allay some of the fears and apprehensions occasioned by *Silent Spring* and the many newspapers and magazine articles that followed in the wake of the book.

The subcommittee staff interviewed 183 scientists and 23 physicians, including officials of the American Medical Association and members of university medical school faculties, who were familiar with the known and potential benefits and hazards in the use of pesticides. Included also were representatives of the three Departments concerned—Agriculture, Interior, and Health, Education, and Welfare. The staff visited, and discussed the operations of sixteen ARS laboratories, five district offices of the Food and Drug Administration, the research facilities of the Public Health Service at Atlanta, Georgia, at Wenatchee, Washington, at Cincinnati, Ohio, and at Bethesda, Maryland (the National Institutes of Health), as well as several research facilities of the Fish and Wildlife Service. Officials were interviewed at fifteen state departments of agriculture, eleven state departments of conservation, five state departments of health, and eight state experiment stations.

The report of this investigation appears in the ARS hearings before the House Appropriations Subcommittee for 1966. The entire report was reprinted by the National Agricultural Chemicals Association for distribution to its members. It drew high praise from Secretary of Agriculture Orville L. Freeman, who said:

> The Surveys and Investigations Staff of the House Committee on Appropriations is to be complimented on the thoroughness of its investigation and the comprehensiveness of its report. . . . It is satisfying to note that the staff's findings indicate that the methods of pest control now being widely advocated have been studied by the Department for many years. . . . The main concern of the Department of Agriculture is to insure the production of a safe, abundant, and wholesome supply of food for the Amer-

ican people. We are pleased to acknowledge a report that recognizes that obligation.

The staff found that the scientists it interviewed had about the same reaction to *Silent Spring* as ARS scientists had had when the book was so popular.

The staff was advised by scientists and by physicians that the book is superficially scientific in that it marshalls a number of accepted scientific facts. However, it is unscientific in (a) drawing incorrect conclusions from unrelated facts, and (b) making implications that are based on possibilities as yet unproved to be actual facts.

The general effect of the report was to reassure its readers concerning pesticides. It was welcomed in the Department of Agriculture because it said what many of the scientists believed, and because it reflected what they had told the investigators. However, it is doubtful if the report had much influence on public opinion, because it was read mostly by those who did not need to be reassured. Also, it did not become available, even as a congressional document, until after the big debate on pesticides had been crowded out of the newspapers and magazines by other subjects.

How Government Operates

In this chapter we have dealt with a great technological advance in pest control. Progress brought problems of adjustment to the new conditions. These problems were discussed by scientists in many technical publications and in semipopular publications, such as the 1952 Yearbook of Agriculture. Scientists sought in vain adequate funds to do the big new jobs that had to be done. They were concerned, and they voiced their concern at meetings and in their publications. Meanwhile the new technology became an accepted pattern of operation on farm and forest. Then a book appeared that challenged the new technology saying that man was using dangerous weapons that he did not know enough about. In spite of its controversial points, it made an eloquent plea for more consideration of the living things in man's environment.

People read the book; many believed it and wrote letters to congressmen, Cabinet members, and newspapers. The President ordered a study of the subject by his science advisers. The Senate held a long series of hearings, and in the end the scientists got the money they had been asking for. They had lost a lot of valuable time, but they would do the best they could to catch up.

Why was this long delay necessary? Had the Department of Agriculture failed to recognize the seriousness of the problem? Perhaps. Was there a failure to communicate this urgent need to the administration and to Congress? Perhaps. Had the administration and Congress failed to listen to the scientists? Perhaps. Was there a failure in communication between the Agricultural Research Service and the public? Perhaps.

Was the long-delayed action in bringing the full force of research to bear on the problem taken because those in high places are quick to respond to a warning from outside the government, but slow to respond to those who have spent their lives in government service? Or was it because those outside of government can apply pressure, and those within cannot? Each reader will doubtless supply his own answers to these questions.

Although the subject of pesticides is still a live one, the great controversy seems to have settled down to a lot of painstaking work by scientists in federal, state, and industrial laboratories all across the country. Reports of their work are encouraging. Some of the answers may be slow in coming, but the work is in good hands.

X

Opportunities Were Never Greater

Agricultural research has come a long way since George Washington laid out his simple experiments to test the value of the few fertilizers that were available to him at Mount Vernon in 1760. At that time the principal occupation in the country was farming, because farmers could produce little more than enough to satisfy the needs of their own families. With stimulation from Europe, leaders in the United States provided support for public education and research to make farming more productive. When the Department of Agriculture was created in 1862, a farm worker could provide enough food and fiber for himself and five others; one hundred years later, a farm worker provided enough for himself and twenty-six others; by 1967, the number had grown to thirty-five. This increase in productivity is one of the marvels of the modern age. Many forces were responsible, but one of the greatest was agricultural research in the state agricultural experiment stations and in the U.S. Department of Agriculture.

Agricultural research is now accepted, together with research in almost every aspect of modern life, as a necessity. The nation is spending approximately a billion dollars a year for agricultural research and development. Nearly half of that sum is spent by industry, whose efforts, with certain notable exceptions, are directed primarily to the development of new products.

ARS is the largest single organization in the $1-billion-a-year

209

agricultural research field. For the fiscal year 1966, it received $148 million and employed 9,310 people in its research activities. These activities cover a broad field, as we have seen in preceding chapters. It may be surprising to learn that the agency still studies soil management and the effects of fertilizers on crop yields, subjects that seemed important to our first President, but Washington himself would not have understood the need for many of the studies now in progress.

Some of the toughest technical problems now facing the nation are under investigation in the Agricultural Research Service. One of these is food poisoning caused by a group of organisms named salmonella that have been traced to several foods, including egg products used with little or no cooking. Salmonella causes a mild form of food poisoning that is particularly prevalent at picnics in warm weather. A step in the control of this problem was taken when two scientists at the Western Utilization Research Laboratory developed a process for commercially pasteurizing the liquid egg whites used in many bakery foods. Although this practice has helped, salmonella is still the most common cause of food poisoning, and is being studied intensively in ARS.

A second problem under intensive study concerns toxic substances produced by certain strains of common molds in foods and feeds. These molds may be present in peanuts, cottonseed, soybeans, corn, rice, and other small grains. This problem was recognized as a major one when nearly 100,000 young turkeys died in England after eating peanut meal imported from Brazil. Investigations disclosed that a toxic substance (aflotoxin) was present.

The first step in dealing with this problem is to prevent the growth of molds on agricultural products before they leave the farm. Keeping these products clean and dry and preventing overheating discourages the growth of molds. ARS has issued a popular publication that gives practical suggestions to farmers on preventing mold damage. It is also cooperating with the

Consumer and Marketing Service of the Department of Agriculture in the strict enforcement of inspection to guarantee that no mold-damaged products are marketed for food or feed. In addition, studies are being made to discover why the toxic substance is produced by molds.

ARS is deeply involved in another relatively new project of wide interest—the search for substances in tobacco that may be associated with cancer. For many years Department of Agriculture plant breeders sought to breed a variety of tobacco especially high in nicotine as a source of nicotine sulphate, an insecticide. At the same time, they tried to breed varieties low in nicotine for smokers. Then the Eastern Utilization Research Division laboratory began experiments to determine the flavor and aroma constituents of tobacco. This work has now been redirected to efforts to break down tobacco smoke into its components and to learn as much about each component as possible. If a constituent of tobacco could be linked with cancer, there is ample reason to believe that scientists could find a way to remove the offensive ingredient.

Glimpses of the Future

Predicting the future is hazardous at best, and the task is even more difficult when the subject of the prediction is an agency of the government. However, several trends are apparent.

One of these is the steady growth of the agency since it acquired its present form in 1953. The scope and complexity of the tasks assigned and the funds to do the work have grown materially. Although federal expenditures for all types of research have grown at a much faster rate, the trend is unmistakable, and there is little evidence to suggest that it will be reversed or even halted for more than short periods.

Since about 1960, a dozen or more large laboratories have been constructed at strategic locations throughout the country. These are small research centers in many cases, staffed by groups of scientists representing several disciplines, all engaged in attacking a common problem. These new laboratories represent the fulfillment of the desire often expressed for "centers of excellence," where scientists can work in an environment that stimulates effort and produces results that often surpass those of a lone worker at an isolated location. In one sense these laboratories represent a trend of decentralization in research and signal an end to further enlargement of the Agricultural Research Center at Beltsville, Maryland. In another sense, they often represent centralization of work in the states, by bringing together several projects that otherwise would have been conducted separately. The new laboratories are usually located on or near the campuses of land-grant universities.

In the future, more ARS work will be on problems that affect people. Research for farmers will also increase, but the proportion will not be as great as for subjects that involve the entire population. Besides problems on food and tobacco, scientists will spend more time on air and water pollution, pesticide residues, human nutrition, beautification, and other topics that affect all citizens.

Research that will benefit farmers primarily will also have great significance for urban dwellers. The cost of food will remain reasonably low (in relation to other costs) only if farmers can continue to hold down production costs, and research can discover more ways to prevent losses and cut costs in marketing. Irrigation research aimed at reducing the amount of water wasted on farms will, if it is successful, reduce costs to farmers and leave more water in streams that supply drinking water to cities. Studies designed to improve the reproduction rate of farm animals may provide basic information of benefit to other species of animals, including man. Knipling's sterility principle will be used to eliminate pest species of birds and mammals as well as insects, and research on leukosis in poultry could profoundly influence research on leukemia in man. Many jobs on farms that require much hand labor, such as harvesting certain fruits and tobacco, will be mechanized. More varieties of plants will be developed with built-in resistance to diseases and insects, with savings to both producers and consumers. Growth regulating chemicals that enable florists to produce tailor-made plants will also be used by millions of home gardeners to give their shrubs a professional appearance. Better lawn grasses and more selective weed-killing chemical will make it possible to have better lawns with less care.

There will be even closer cooperation with the state experiment stations, if present trends continue. Differences between the states and ARS are relatively minor, and ways will be found to smooth them out. One difference that developed in the early 1960's concerned the large new laboratories established by ARS in the states. The station directors believe that they should have a larger part in planning the work to be done at these regional laboratories, which will often be giving major attention to matters of special importance to the states in which they are located. There are indications that ARS will give the stations a larger role in planning the work of such laboratories, while retaining control of funds as required by Congress. The annual threat to close several field stations (an irritation to station directors, explained in Chapter VII) will probably be abandoned. If the threat continues, it will come from the Secretary of Agriculture or the Bureau of the Budget, but there is reason to believe that the executive branch will give up on this effort.

In recent years ARS has learned how to work more effectively with Congress, and there is every indication that it will continue in this direction. Before 1960 the agency suffered from two handicaps in getting appropriations, especially for new activities: the desire for a balanced budget at the White House and in Congress, and also the desire of the agency itself to continue development of the Beltsville Agricultural Research Center by constructing new buildings to house part of the new work proposed. ARS was encouraged in this effort by the research advisory committees, but it was impossible to sell the idea to Congress. Research appropriations to the Atomic Energy Commission, the National Aeronautics and Space Administration, and the National Institutes of Health soared, while those for ARS increased at a snail's pace. The missions of these agencies vary too much to draw parallels, but ARS officials could not help but wonder if wider dispersal of its funds in carefully selected states would help its cause in Congress. One friendly member of Congress dropped such a hint. ARS followed the suggestion and promptly got money for a laboratory it needed very much. It is not likely that this lesson will be forgotten.

Emphasis on Basic Research

Research designed to increase yields in crops and livestock will be discussed more openly in the future than it has been for many years. This is the type of research that makes production more efficient and more certain through improvement of crops and livestock, wise use of fertilizer, pest control, and new ideas such as planting cotton in rows nine inches apart with a grain drill, instead of the traditional rows about three and a half feet apart. Despite the fact that this kind of research was in large measure responsible for the agricultural revolution in the United States, there was a period of several years when, because of surpluses, it had to be discussed discreetly. In justifying such research to the Bureau of the Budget and to Congress and in reporting it to the public, ARS portrayed it as research to promote efficient production, a cause with which no one could quarrel. For defensive reasons, the official designation of this activity was changed from "production research" to "farm research." Fortunately for the country, this research was never cut back drastically by Congress, even when it was unpopular with those who worried about surpluses. Some of the large increases for 1966 and 1967 were for farm research, and this trend will almost surely continue.

Basic research will receive more attention in the future, in both the Agricultural Research Service and the state stations. With a few exceptions, U.S. research before World War I was based upon discoveries of laws and principles by Europeans. The war disrupted work at many research centers in England, France, and Germany, and some of the large universities here began to stress basic research. Although research in the U.S. Department of Agriculture was oriented from the beginning to practical problems, there were occasional discoveries of a basic nature, some of which have been discussed.

Basic research in the Department and at the state stations received a big boost from the Bankhead-Jones Act of 1935 and has grown slowly since that time. In 1957, ARS began organizing pioneering research laboratories in most of its research divisions. This designation does not mean a separate building or physical facilities. It is a way of giving organizational and financial recognition to scientists who are doing first-rate basic research in areas that can be clearly identified. One of these laboratories may have on its staff only one or two senior scientists, with one or more assistants. These laboratories provide freedom for outstanding scientists to follow whatever leads they choose. They have no specific goals or deadlines and are freed of the task of making frequent progress reports and justification statements and doing other administrative chores that are part of supervisory positions. Compensation for these positions ranges all the way from that of a GS-12 (about $12,-500 a year) to the top bracket for scientists and engineers (about $26,000). At one time the head of one of the pioneering laboratories was receiving more salary than the administrator. In addition to research by these special groups, each research division conducts basic research in support of its objectives. About one-third of all ARS research is now basic, and the proportion will increase in the future.

One of the trends in ARS research is more emphasis on long-range plans. The purpose of such plans is to spell out needs for research, define goals, and make recommendations on manpower requirements to reach the goals.

Although several studies on research needs for the future have been made in the Department of Agriculture, the most comprehensive one was completed late in 1966. With the help of several task forces, a committee of Department and state station representatives spent a year considering future needs for research and making recommendations for meeting those needs. The report, "A National Program for Agricultural Research," deals with every line of research in the Department and the stations, giving its status at the time the study was made and the projected needs for 1972 and 1977. The committee considered all agricultural research needs, making no effort to decide which work should be done by the states, which by the Department of Agriculture, and which by industry. The study assumes a high degree of coordination in planning and carrying on research in the future.

Long-range studies of research requirements always anticipate expanding the work and enlarging the staffs to get it done. The most recent study follows the same pattern. It breaks down future needs into ninety-one problem areas and suggests targets for each of these, in man-years, for 1972 and 1977. Recommended increases in manpower for 1972 and 1977 are 38 per cent and 76 per cent above the level for 1965, respectively. In relation to growth from 1960 to 1966, these estimates do not appear excessive. (The last time ARS made a careful appraisal of research needs for the future, it called for similar large increases, and for that reason the figures were never released.)

What's Ahead in Regulatory Work?

An interesting development is taking place in livestock production that will affect ARS regulatory work in the future. The country seems to be headed for a day when every farm animal will be identified not by name but by number. If this takes place, it will be a big help to agencies charged with protecting the health of our livestock.

The idea of identifying farm animals by numbers and letters originated in the campaign to eradicate brucellosis of cattle and hogs. As explained in Chapter IV, ranchers in the West were not willing to spend the time necessary to round up large herds of semiwild cattle to have them tested for presence of the disease. Workers in the Washington State Department of Agriculture conceived the idea of identifying each animal with a plastic tag as it was sent to market. The numbers and letters identified not only the animal, but also the state and county from which it came. The practice has worked so well that officials are now thinking of expanding it to include identification of all farm animals except poultry.

Knowing the origin of animals that show symptoms of disease when they are inspected at the large stockyards before slaughter would be a tremendous help to state and federal authorities. Instead of isolating the animal and dealing with it individually, they could check immediately with the shipper and his local veterinarian for signs of trouble in the herd. Quick action can often prevent an epidemic and save thousands of dollars for the owner.

Identifying farm animals would be a natural outgrowth of the concept of state and federal livestock officials that their job is to keep livestock healthy, rather than to cure sick animals or eradicate a disease. This concept was responsible for the campaign to eradicate hog cholera, so that farmers would no longer have to live with the constant threat of having their herds exposed to it. Identification is required in the purchase, sale, and transportation of all dogs and cats used for research purposes. In recognition of the increased emphasis being given to this concept, the name of ARS's Animal Disease Eradication Division was changed in 1965 to Animal Health Division.

A major change in shipping methods will present new problems to ARS plant quarantine workers. The transportation industry is mechanizing the loading and unloading of cargo by using large containers that permit one man and one crane to unload a 6,000-ton vessel in ten hours. Standardized containers are large boxes 8 feet high, 8 feet wide, and 10, 20, 30, or 40 feet long. With wheels, they can be rolled on or off ships built especially to transport the containers. They will fit into railroad cars, trucks, and cargo planes, as well as ships.

Use of containers offers several advantages, in addition to savings in labor. For many agricultural products the big boxes will prevent damage to the product, eliminate pilferage, reduce insurance and shipping rates, and speed the movement of cargo. It is this latter advantage that will present new problems to those whose job it is to prevent foreign pests from entering this country.

To utilize the advantages of containers, they will be shipped direct from the point of origin to final destination without being opened. That means the opportunity to inspect the contents at ports of entry, begun in 1910, will soon be lost for all cargo in containers. ARS officials regard this as a major problem that must be dealt with on a large scale by 1970, and they have already begun to prepare for it.

One step is to arrange with foreign countries to have ARS inspectors located at strategic points abroad to work with local quarantine officials to insure that products exported to the U.S. are free of pests. This plan has worked well for several years for bulbs shipped here from Holland, and is being expanded to cover other countries.

Even if such plans prove successful, they will be only the first step in protecting producers and consumers here. Research now in progress is aimed at developing a safe, effective, and economical method to eliminate pests inside the containers without damaging the product or leaving harmful residues. Possibilities being investigated include low-oxygen atmospheres, fumigation, radioactivity, and infrared rays. Several major cargo distribution points will be established throughout the United States;

inspectors will be located at these points, as well as at the large ports.

Research and regulatory work have been carried out side by side in the Department of Agriculture since the Bureau of Animal Industry was created in 1884. Several attempts to separate these functions have failed. To separate or not to separate—is one of the questions that must be decided by every new Secretary of Agriculture. On the surface, there appear to be many reasons for concentrating all research in one agency and all regulatory duties in another, but for the reasons given in Chapter III Secretaries of Agriculture Benson and Freeman retained both functions in the Agricultural Research Service. Some of Freeman's advisers believe that research and regulatory work should be separated, if not by Freeman, then by his successor. But regardless of its organizational structure, regulatory work will continue to depend upon research to guide its action programs and will improve its effectiveness only as fast as research provides the tools.

With new tools, regulatory work should be able to conquer some of its old enemies, such as the fire ant in the South and perhaps even the gypsy moth in the Northeast. Better coordination of its efforts with other federal agencies through the Federal Committee on Pest Control will help to forestall charges that ARS is interested only in getting rid of pests, regardless of the costs to other forms of life. The added emphasis now given to keeping the public informed will help to explain the need for some of the less popular phases of regulatory activities, if top officials heed the advice of their information workers, but only time can tell if this will take place.

Exporting Knowledge

Forecasts of changes in ARS objectives and operations have dealt thus far with the impact of those changes in the United States. There is no reason, however, to assume that knowledge of better methods to grow food or to nourish the human body will stop at our borders. This knowledge will be used by people everywhere.

With so many people in the world living on the brink of starvation, the challenge to agricultural research has never been greater. The challenge is first of all to help U.S. farmers to produce an abundance for the growing population at home and to help the developing nations learn to grow enough food so that they will no longer be threatened with hunger and starvation. The Service is in a strategic position to join with other agencies in accepting this challenge.

Aid to developing countries of the Free World is an established policy of the United States. Although there will doubtless be urgent needs for food, medical supplies, and other direct aid from this country for several years, the greatest need is for knowledge that will make it possible for the needy nations to utilize their people and their resources to increase their own production of food and other necessities.

It is now generally recognized that aid to developing countries must give first priority to agricultural development. Industrial, economic, and cultural advancement must rest upon a solid foundation that only a stable agriculture can provide. There is also general agreement that the only way to achieve a stable agriculture in the developing nations is through science and technology.

Agricultural knowledge has been exported for centuries. In the 1870's Professor William S. Clark, President of the Massachusetts Agricultural College, organized an agricultural college in Japan and patterned it after the land-grant colleges of the United States. Agricultural missionaries have introduced improved farm practices in many countries. Technical assistance was one of the key points of the Marshall Plan, which helped the countries of Western Europe recover from the effects of World War II. Point 4 of the Plan dealt with lending scientists as well as food and dollars. Scientists from the Agricultural Research

Service helped to develop improved food and feed crops in many countries and taught agricultural technicians in the Near East to control locusts.

Since that time the idea has continued to spread. Both the Ford and Rockefeller foundations have been active in Latin America, and both have strong groups in India, Pakistan, and other parts of Asia, cooperating with agricultural officials of the countries involved. The Inter-American Institute of Agricultural Sciences has been operating for many years in Central America and is reaching down into South America. Some of the results have been impressive. With the help of Rockefeller scientists, for example, Mexico increased the average yield of wheat from eleven and a half bushels per acre in 1943 to thirty-three bushels per acre in 1963. In the same period Mexico became self-sufficient in both wheat and corn.

The original method for exporting knowledge was to send scientists abroad for periods ranging up to two years or more. They usually worked with local scientists at their research stations, some of which were poorly equipped. This practice has continued but has been supplemented by a large-scale program for bringing foreign students and scientists to the United States for observation and study. Many remain to work for a year at one of the state experiment stations or in ARS, and several hundred are enrolled for regular courses at the land-grant universities. Tours are arranged to show the visitors how research is done and how extension agents take results of research directly to farm people.

The International Agricultural Development Service was created in the U.S. Department of Agriculture in 1963 to coordinate all matters dealing with developing countries and the training of visitors from those countries. In 1966, this agency planned and conducted tours for 2,187 agricultural workers, mostly from countries where the Agency for International Development has missions. Most of the land-grant universities now have contracts with that agency to work with developing countries in research and education. An example is the contract with North Carolina State University on the fertilizer requirements of countries in Latin America. This contract calls for testing thousands of soil samples and making recommendations for application of lime and fertilizers. Soil testing laboratories have been built and equipped, and local workers are taught to make the soil tests and interpret them. Other land-grant university scientists are working in South America, Asia, and Africa to improve farming.

The Agricultural Research Service also is participating on a broad front in the export of knowledge. Its scientists are breeding improved varieties of such food crops as edible legumes and rice and other grains, introducing better animal husbandry, and developing methods of insect control, irrigation, and soil improvement. There is no doubt of the effectiveness of such efforts when they are supported by a determination of the developing nations to help themselves. Results of the Rockefeller Foundation work in Mexico show what can be done. There are many other examples. A 1965 Department of Agriculture study revealed that several developing countries had increased agricultural output in the period 1948–63 at rates of increase that were higher than had been attained in the United States in the periods of our greatest growth.

It has been said that the future belongs to those who prepare for it. The Agricultural Research Service is in a most strategic position to join with agricultural scientists in the states, in industry and private foundations, and in other countries to help shape the future for the benefit of all people everywhere.

Appendix A. The Agricultural Research Service as a Career

How to Apply for a Position in ARS

Practically all of the positions in ARS are filled through the civil service system, and appointments are made from lists of eligible persons who have passed civil service examinations. In many cases a bachelor's degree from a recognized college or university is the principal requirement for placement on a list for a professional position. Applicants must fill out a form, listing education and work experience, if any. These forms are available at many post offices and at college or university placement bureaus.

The largest number of applicants enter government service under one of the various entrance examinations. The one most widely used throughout the federal government is the Federal Service Entrance Examination (FSEE), but only jobs in the ARS management divisions and the Information Division are filled from this examination. Research divisions recruit from examinations for (1) agricultural research scientist, (2) chemist, and (3) engineer. Regulatory divisions recruit from examinations for (1) plant pest control inspector, (2) plant quarantine inspector, and (3) veterinarian. A written test is required for the FSEE, but no test is required for the others. No work experience is necessary for the entrance examinations, but extra credit is given for pertinent experience.

Because research problems are so complex and the equipment used is so sophisticated, ARS places special emphasis on recruiting scientists who have had graduate training, preferably those with a Ph.D. degree. There are some openings for applicants with B.S. and M.S. degrees if they have made above-average grades.

Announcements of civil service examinations are usually posted in post offices and other federal buildings. They are also available from college or university placement bureaus. If not available from these sources, they may be obtained from the Civil Service Commission, Washington, D.C., 20415, or the ARS Personnel Division, Federal Center Building, Hyattsville, Maryland, 20781. Be sure to specify the examination you wish to take. ARS is a large organization. In a normal year it requires more than 300 new research employees, about 100 plant pest and plant quarantine inspectors, and about 50 veterinarians.

Training Opportunities

New employees in the management and regulatory divisions immediately begin an intensive course of training to prepare them for the work they are to do. This training is full-time, and in most of the divisions it runs for six months, although in some cases it may last longer. During this period the new employee has an opportunity to become acquainted with several phases of work in a division, branch, or section, and will attend numerous orientation sessions. At the end of the training period employees are assigned to regular positions. Those whose work is satisfactory at the end of the first year are usually promoted to the next highest grade (actually from GS-5 to GS-7), which means an increase of about $1,000 a year.

The research divisions have less formal training programs for new employees, but in a sense every young scientist is a trainee. His first assignment as a junior scientist may be to serve as an assistant to a senior scientist who plans and conducts his own work with very little supervision, an ideal learning situation for a young scientist. Some of the research divisions have special summer trainee programs, beginning the summer following graduation from high school and continuing each summer until graduation from college. Through its cooperation with the land-grant universities, ARS and the universities offer many opportunities for part-time work for graduate students. Details can be obtained from the various departments of the universities, the ARS Personnel Division, or direct from the research divisions. Their addresses are given in Chapter II.

Opportunities for training are by no means limited to the first year of employment or to those enrolled in graduate schools. ARS carries on a broad training program that embraces all employees from typists to top administrators. In fiscal year 1966 nearly 10,000 employees—more than half of the total in ARS—took courses to improve their effectiveness. Three-fourths of these took courses given by ARS or other government personnel in what is called in-service training. The remainder took courses given by instructors operating independently or as staff members of an educational institution. Most of these formal courses are for relatively short periods, but in 1966, thirty-five employees spent 120 days or more in training. Under special conditions an employee may be permitted to spend a full academic year at a university at no cost to himself if the administrator determines it is in the best interests of the agency. Needless to say, such cases are rare, but ARS has had several in recent years.

Employee training in ARS is conducted under authority of the Government Employees' Training Act, Public Law 85-507, and falls into five major categories: (1) orientation; (2) clerical, stenographic, or other office training; (3) supervisory and management training; (4) scientific, technical, and other professional training; and (5) craft, trade, aide, technician, and custodial training.

Career Opportunities

Because of its size and the broad field of work it covers, ARS offers unusually good opportunities for scientific careers. It covers most of the biological sciences from agronomy to zoology, in addition to chemistry and engineering. Chapter II gives an idea of the broad range of activities and of the many kinds of scientists required.

Most of the research in ARS is carried on in an environment that is particularly favorable to study and exploration. In recent years many crowded and poorly equipped facilities have been replaced with large modern buildings and equipment. Because of extensive cooperation with the state universities, a large share of research is at or near educational and cultural centers. Research in large metropolitan areas such as Washington, D.C., Philadelphia, Peoria,

San Francisco, and New Orleans, is conducted in suburban locations, with ample parking space and other attractions that only open spaces can offer.

Excellent library facilities are available to ARS scientists. The National Agricultural Library, located in Washington, is the largest and most complete agricultural library in the world. It contains more than 1,200,000 volumes on agriculture and related sciences.

Opportunity to publish is another attraction offered by ARS. Young scientists are encouraged to write papers on their work and submit them to journals of their choice. Supervisors give aid and encouragement in the preparation of research reports.

ARS has an excellent record on promotions. It originated the promotion plan described in Chapter II, by which scientists may be promoted to the highest civil service grades without having to give up research and becoming administrators. Scientists may now move upward either on the administrative ladder or solely on the basis of their competence as scientists.

An additional attraction is the opportunity for public service. The satisfaction that comes from a lifetime of service in science is well expressed in a letter to the administrator from Dr. Eugene S. Schultz, who retired in 1953 after thirty-nine years of Department of Agriculture research. His work resulted in the development of several new varieties of potatoes resistant to late blight and mild mosaic, two of the worst diseases of potatoes. Dr. Schultz's work made him a world authority on virus diseases of potatoes. His letter to the administrator said in part: "You may be interested to know that I thoroughly enjoyed my work in the Department, which to my knowledge is second to no other institution in granting freedom for the prosecution of research and for rendering unlimited service. I agree completely with one of my former executive officers, who remarked that he always regarded it a great mistake for a research worker to leave the Department before he was ready for retirement."

This letter is one man's answer to the belief prevalent in some colleges and universities that government service does not offer a satisfactory career to students who show promise of becoming exceptional scientists. It also expresses the feeling of many scientists in the Agricultural Research Service and the state agricultural experiment stations.

Appendix B. Statistics on Appropriations and Personnel

Estimated Appropriations (Including Funds for Construction, Salaries, and Expenses) for Agricultural Research Administration (Fiscal Years 1946–53) and Agricultural Research Service (Fiscal Years 1954–67)

(In millions of dollars)

	Research	Disease and pest control	Total
1946	19.8	14.6	34.4
1947	22.9	16.7	39.6
1948	27.1	16.7	43.9
1949	31.8	18.2	50.0
1950	32.4	20.0	52.4
1951	31.0	18.4	49.5
1952	31.1	19.0	50.2
1953	31.4	18.8	50.2
1954	32.4	17.9	50.3
1955	37.0	18.3	55.3
1956	40.2	20.6	60.8
1957	54.2	29.7	83.9
1958	60.0	30.0	90.0
1959	63.3	52.9	116.2
1960	68.3	49.8	118.0
1961	75.0	53.9	128.9
1962	81.4	58.0	139.5
1963	92.9	59.5	152.4
1964	110.8	64.3	175.2
1965	134.4	71.2	205.6
1966	144.1	75.5	219.6
1967	151.0	80.1	231.1

Distribution of Personnel by Activities
Calendar Years 1946–65

	Research			Plant- and animal-disease and pest control			All personnel		
	Full-time	Other	Total	Full-time	Other	Total	Full-time	Other	Total
1946	4,587	568	5,155	2,893	501	3,394	7,480	1,069	8,549
1947	4,640	622	5,262	3,724	283	4,007	8,364	905	9,269
1948	5,146	557	5,703	4,068	271	4,339	9,214	828	10,042
1949	5,336	537	5,873	4,897	502	5,399	10,233	1,039	11,272
1950	5,245	678	5,923	4,237	365	4,602	9,482	1,043	10,525
1951	4,854	514	5,368	3,562	330	3,892	8,416	844	9,260
1952	4,961	664	5,626	2,744	240	2,984	7,705	904	8,609
1953	4,902	716	5,618	3,268	215	3,483	8,170	931	9,101
1954	5,553	677	6,230	3,261	979	4,240	8,814	1,656	10,470
1955	5,991	627	6,618	3,615	4,495	8,110	9,606	5,122	14,728
1956	6,350	689	7,039	4,194	3,608	7,802	10,544	4,297	14,841
1957	6,728	674	7,402	4,499	3,807	8,306	11,227	4,481	15,708
1958	7,072	636	7,708	4,999	3,637	8,636	12,071	4,273	16,344
1959	7,182	691	7,873	4,665	91	4,756	11,847	782	12,629
1960	7,391	588	7,979	4,772	145	4,917	12,163	733	12,896
1961	7,974	546	8,250	4,873	124	4,997	12,847	670	13,517
1962	8,036	523	8,559	5,353	149	5,502	13,389	672	14,061
1963	8,439	525	8,964	5,334	209	5,543	13,773	734	14,507
1964	8,493	489	8,982	5,430	503	5,933	13,923	992	14,915
1965	8,833	477	9,310	5,485	262	5,747	14,318	739	15,057

Appendix C. Principal Field Stations of the ARS

ALABAMA
  Auburn
    Regional Animal Disease Research Laboratory
    Tillage Machinery Laboratory

ALASKA
  Palmer—Alaska Experiment Station

ARIZONA
  Glendale—Southwest Poultry Experiment Station
  Mesa—Entomology Research Laboratory
  Phoenix—Cotton Research Center
  Tempe (*Phoenix*)—Soil and Water Conservation Research
    Laboratory
  Tucson
    Western Cotton Insect Laboratory
    Southwest Range and Watershed Research Center

CALIFORNIA
  Albany—Western Utilization Research Laboratory
  Brawley—Southwestern Irrigation Field Station
  Chico—U.S. Plant Introduction Station
  Fresno—U.S. Horticultural Field Station
  Indio—U.S. Date Garden
  La Jolla—U.S. Horticultural Field Station
  Pasadena—Fruit and Vegetable Chemical Laboratory
  Pomona—Western Citrus Fruit Laboratory

Riverside—U.S. Salinity Laboratory
Salinas—U.S. Agricultural Experiment Station
Shafter—U.S. Cotton Field Station

COLORADO
Akron—Central Great Plains Field Station
Denver—Blue Tongue Virus Research Laboratory
Fort Collins
  National Seed Storage Laboratory
  Nitrogen Laboratory
Greeley—Colorado Potato Field Station

DISTRICT OF COLUMBIA—National Arboretum

FLORIDA
Brooksville—Beef Cattle Research Station
Canal Point—Sugar Plant Field Station
Gainesville—Insects Affecting Man and Animal Research
  Laboratory
Miami—U.S. Plant Introduction Garden
Olustee—Naval Stores Station
Orlando—U.S. Horticultural Field Station
Winter Haven—Southeastern Utilization Research Laboratory

GEORGIA
Albany—Pecan Field Station
Athens—Southeastern Poultry Field Station
Byron—Regional Tree Fruit and Nut Research Laboratory
Fleming—Southeastern Tidewater Field Station
Fort Valley—Horticultural Field Station
Savannah—U.S. Plant Introduction Garden
Tifton
  Georgia Coastal Plain Experiment Station
  Grain Insect Laboratory
Watkinsville—Southern Piedmont Soil Conservation Research
  Center

HAWAII
Honolulu—Fruit Fly Laboratory

IDAHO

Boise—Northwestern Watershed Research Center
Dubois—Western Sheep Breeding Laboratory
Twin Falls—Soil and Water Conservation Research Laboratory

ILLINOIS

Carbondale—Small Fruit Research Station
Peoria—Northern Utilization Research Laboratory
Urbana
    U.S. Regional Soybean Laboratory
    Soil and Water Conservation Research Laboratory

INDIANA

Vincennes—Entomology Field Laboratory

IOWA

Ames
    National Animal Disease Laboratory
    Regional Plant Introduction Station
Ankeny—The European Corn Borer Research Laboratory

LOUISIANA

Bogalusa—U.S. Field Station for Tung Investigations
Houma—Sugar Plant Station
Jeanerette—Iberia Experiment Station
Lake Charles—Gulf Coast Marsh and Rice Field Mosquito Investigation Laboratory
New Orleans—Southern Utilization Research Laboratory
Shreveport—U.S. Pecan Field Station

MAINE

Presque Isle—Maine Potato Handling Research Center

MARYLAND

Beltsville—Agricultural Research Center
Glenn Dale—Plant Introduction Station

MICHIGAN

East Lansing—Regional Poultry Laboratory

MINNESOTA

East Grand Forks—Red River Valley Potato Research Center

Minneapolis—St. Anthony Falls Hydraulic Laboratory
Morris—Soil and Water Conservation Laboratory

MISSISSIPPI
Gulfport—Plant Pest Control Facilities
Meridian—U.S. Sugar Crops Field Station
Oxford—U.S. Sedimentation Laboratory
State College
South Central Poultry Research Laboratory
Boll Weevil Research Laboratory
Stoneville—Cotton-Ginning Research Laboratory

MISSOURI
Columbia—North Central Watershed Research Center

MONTANA
Bozeman—Entomology Research Laboratory
Miles City—Range Livestock Experiment Station
Sidney—Soil and Water Research Laboratory

NEBRASKA
Clay Center—Meat Animal Research Center
Fort Robinson—Beef Cattle Husbandry
Hastings—Soil and Water Conservation Research Laboratory

NEW JERSEY
Moorestown—Entomology Research Station

NEW MEXICO
Albuquerque—Parasite Laboratory
Las Cruces—Range Research
Mesilla Park—Southwestern Cotton-Ginning Laboratory

NEW YORK
Ithaca
Fur Animal Station
U.S. Plant-Soil-Nutrition Laboratory
Plum Island—Animal Disease Laboratory

NORTH CAROLINA
Oxford—Tobacco Research Laboratory
Whiteville—Border Belt Tobacco Station

NORTH DAKOTA
Fargo—Metabolism and Radiation Research Laboratory
Mandan—Northern Great Plains Field Station

OHIO
Coshocton—Soil and Water Conservation Experiment Station
Delaware—Shade Tree and Ornamental Plant Laboratory

OKLAHOMA
Chickasha—Southern Great Plains Watershed Research Center
Fort Reno—Beef Cattle Research Laboratory
Woodward—Southern Great Plains Field Station

OREGON
Burns—Squaw Butte-Harney Station
Forest Grove—Agricultural Engineering and Entomology Research Investigations

PENNSYLVANIA
University Park—U.S. Regional Pasture Research Laboratory
Wyndmoor—Eastern Utilization Research Laboratory

SOUTH CAROLINA
Charleston—Vegetable Breeding Laboratory
Clemson—Cotton-Ginning Research Laboratory
Florence—Soil and Water Conservation Research Laboratory

SOUTH DAKOTA
Brookings—Northern Grain Insects Research Laboratory
Newell—Irrigation and Dryland Field Station

TENNESSEE
Greenville—Tobacco Experiment Station
Knoxville—U.S. Cotton Field Station
Lewisburg—Dairy Experiment Station

TEXAS
Beaumont—Rice Pasture Experiment Station
Big Spring—Soil and Water Conservation Research Station
Brownsville—Entomology Research Laboratory
Bushland—Southwestern Great Plains Field Station

College Station—Southwestern Veterinary Toxicological
Livestock Insect Research Laboratory
Kerrville
Insect Experiment Station
Veterinary Toxicology Laboratory
Lubbock—South Plains Research and Extension Center
Mission—Screwworm Research Laboratory
Temple-Riesel—Soil and Water Management Investigations
Weslaco
U.S. Fruit and Vegetable Products Utilization Laboratory
Horticultural and Soils Laboratory

UTAH
Logan—Crops Research Laboratory

VIRGINIA
Front Royal—Beef Cattle Research Station
Holland—Tidewater Research Station

VIRGIN ISLANDS—Farm Electrification

WASHINGTON
Prosser—Irrigation Experiment Station
Pullman—Ends-Parasite Pioneering Research Laboratory
Wenatchee—Washington Tree Fruit Experiment Station
Yakima
Packaging and Transportation Research
Entomology Research Laboratory

WISCONSIN
Madison—Barley and Malt Laboratory

WYOMING
Cheyenne—Horticultural Field Station

PUERTO RICO
Mayaguez—Federal Experiment Station (subtropical plant research)

Appendix D. Research Contracts

Contracts for research by public and private institutions provide an opportunity for ARS to improve its service to the nation by utilizing the knowledge and experience of many scientists who would not otherwise be available. Authority for contracted research was contained in the Research and Marketing Act of 1946, but it was not widely used by ARS until recent years, when substantial increases in funds became available. A sampling of contracts made in 1965 and 1966 for research to develop new or improved uses for farm products suggests the broad field covered.

Archer Daniels Midland Company, Minneapolis, Minnesota— To develop a process for converting animal fats into highly soluble detergents that will not produce foam in streams.

*Swift and Company, Chicago, Illinois—*To develop a commercial method to utilize beef tallow in making soluble detergents.

*Houdry Process and Chemical Company, Marcus Hook, Pennsylvania—*To study chemicals capable of modifying temperatures of burning cigarettes, in an effort to establish a relationship between various cigarette temperatures and the chemical composition of smoke.

*University of Kentucky Research Foundation, Lexington, Kentucky—*To analyze cigarette smoke for the presence of potentially injurious substances that might be formed during smoking and, if such substances are found, to determine their chemical and biological properties.

*South Dakota Agricultural Experiment Station, Brookings, South Dakota—*To conduct research on molds that grow on commercial grains, in an effort to determine to what extent the food and feed value of grain is damaged by common molds.

University of Illinois, Urbana, Illinois—To study the processing techniques necessary to convert soybean oil into more solid shortenings and margarines and to improve its flavor stability.

Fabrics Research Laboratories, Dedham, Massachusetts—To develop improved coated cotton fabrics for use in tents, awnings, tarpaulins, leatherette upholstery, and many other products.

Illinois Institute of Technology, Chicago, Illinois—To study changes that occur in wheat flour molecules during various steps in the baking process, in an effort to identify flours that give uniform baking performance.

Malicki Laboratories, Inc., Chicago, Illinois—To investigate ways to speed up the freeze drying of fruit juices and other liquid foods and thereby reduce their cost.

American Foundation for Biological Research, Madison, Wisconsin—To try to establish relationships between changes in tenderness of poultry meat and such processes as freezing, thawing, and cooking.

Harris Research Laboratories, Inc., Washington, D.C.—To develop low-cost chemical finishes that will make wool resistant to stains and soiling and also water repellent.

New York University, New York City—To improve durability and wash-wear qualities of cotton by treating cotton fibers and fabrics with chemicals that will develop into polymers (long-chain molecules) with better wearing quality.

Bibliography

CARSON, RACHEL. *Silent Spring*. Boston: Houghton Mifflin, 1962.

DUPREE, A. HUNTER. *Science in the Federal Government: A History of Policies and Activities to 1940*. Cambridge, Mass.: Belknap Press of Harvard University Press, 1957.

Fund Support to the State Agricultural Experiment Stations. Washington, D.C.: Association of State Universities and Land Grant Colleges, 1964.

HARDING, T. SWANN. *Two Blades of Grass: A History of Science in the United States Department of Agriculture*. Norman, Okla.: University of Oklahoma Press, 1947.

HAWORTH, PAUL L. *George Washington, Country Gentleman*. Indianapolis: Bobbs-Merrill, 1925.

Hoover Commission Report, U.S. Commission on Organization of the Executive Branch of the Government. New York: McGraw-Hill, 1949.

Scientific Aspects of Pest Control: A Symposium, February 1–3, 1966. (NAS–NRC Publication 1402.) Washington, D.C.: National Academy of Sciences–National Research Council, 1966. This is a complete and authoritative reference on pesticides, giving the complete text of twenty-nine papers by recognized authorities.

Service Monographs of U.S. Government. Washington, D.C.: Institute for Government Research, Brookings Institution, 1927–30. Because of its age and limited scope, this series, which includes one volume on each of the scientific bureaus of the U.S. Department of Agriculture, is useful mainly for its historical value.

STEINHAUS, EDWARD A. *Insect Pathology: An Advanced Treatise*. 2 vols. New York: Academic Press, 1963.

WHITTEN, JAMIE L. *That We May Live*. Princeton, N.J.: Van Nostrand, 1966. This book presents the case for chemical pesticides and, in some respects, is an answer to Rachel Carson's *Silent Spring*. It is a strong defense of agricultural scientists who are responsible for research and regulatory actions on pesticides.

Government Publications

After a Hundred Years. (The Yearbook of Agriculture, 1962.) Washington, D.C.: U.S. Government Printing Office, 1962.

BAKER, GLADYS L., *et al. Century of Service: The First 100 Years of the United States Department of Agriculture.* Washington, D.C.: U.S. Government Printing Office, 1963. The most authoritative history of the Department. Because this volume covers so many activities, it necessarily reports only the highlights of research.

Basic Research, Applied Research, and Development in Industry, 1963. (National Science Foundation "Survey of Science Resources Series.") Washington, D.C.: U.S. Government Printing Office, 1966.

Consumers All. (The Yearbook of Agriculture, 1965.) Washington, D.C.: U.S. Government Printing Office, 1965. Hundreds of short articles that consumers can use on camping, cooking, home decorating, home equipment, home building, family finances, and many other subjects.

Food. (The Yearbook of Agriculture, 1959.) Washington, D.C.: U.S. Government Printing Office, 1959.

Insects. (The Yearbook of Agriculture, 1952.) Washington, D.C.: U.S. Government Printing Office, 1952.

MOORE, ERNEST G. "Men Who Went Before," in *Science in Farming.* (The Yearbook of Agriculture, 1943–47.) Washington, D.C.: U.S. Government Printing Office, 1947.

A National Program of Research for Agriculture: Report of a State-Federal Study of Research Needs. Washington, D.C.: U.S. Department of Agriculture, 1966. The most recent and comprehensive study of research needs in agriculture.

Pest Control by Chemical, Biological, Genetic, and Physical Means: A Symposium at the December, 1964, Meeting of the American Association for the Advancement of Science, Montreal. (ARS 33-110.) Washington, D.C.: U.S. Department of Agriculture, 1966.

Research in Agriculture: A Symposium Sponsored by U.S. Department of Agriculture and the National Academy of Sciences. Washington, D.C.: 1966.

State Agricultural Experiment Stations: A History of Research Policy and Procedure. (U.S. Department of Agriculture Miscellaneous Publication No. 904.) Washington, D.C.: U.S. Government Printing Office, 1962.

TRUE, A. C. *A History of Agricultural Experimentation and Research in the United States from 1607 to 1925.* (U.S. Department of Agriculture Miscellaneous Publication No. 251.) Washington, D.C.: U.S. Government Printing Office, 1937. This is the most detailed history of agricultural research in the United States for the period covered.

It is now out of print but should be available at college and university libraries, as well as at most public libraries in large cities. This work was invaluable in the preparation of Chapter I.

U.S. Congress (House). *Department of Agriculture and Related Agencies Appropriation Bill, 1967.* 88th Congress, 2d Session, Report 1446.

————. *Effects, Uses, Control, and Research of Agricultural Pesticides: A Report by the Surveys and Investigations Staff, Subcommittee on Department of Agriculture of the Committee on Appropriations.*

————. *Hearings on Department of Agriculture Appropriation Bill.* Agricultural Research Administration, 1946–53: Agricultural Research Service, 1954–67.

U.S. Congress (Senate). *Department of Agriculture and Related Agencies Appropriation Bill, 1967.* 89th Congress, 2d Session, Report 1370.

————. *Interagency Coordination in Environmental Hazards (Pesticides). Hearings Before the Subcommittee on Reorganization and International Organizations of the Committee on Government Operations.* 88th Congress. Washington, D.C.: U.S. Government Printing Office, 1964. The complete hearings comprise eleven parts and five appendixes, a total of sixteen volumes. Part 1 is probably the most useful. Parts 1 and 2 of the appendix include material prepared by the Agricultural Research Service for the President's Science Advisory Committee's report on the use of pesticides. The material covers all pesticide activities in the Agricultural Research Service and fills 704 printed pages.

Use of Pesticides: A Report of the President's Science Advisory Committee. Washington, D.C.: U.S. Government Printing Office, 1963.

Index

240